Sunshine
on my mind

Philip Yorke

MASHIACH PUBLISHING

philipyorke.org

First published in Great Britain in 2023.

0062023

Copyright © Philip Yorke 2023

Mashiach Publishing

The Author asserts the moral right to
be identified as the author of this work.

ISBN 9 78 1 739 4211 0 6

Set in 12 point Baskerville and Baskerville SemiBold

philipyorke.org

Dedicated to the Longbone siblings:
Ann, Ian, Brenda and Maureen

No longer with us, but always in our hearts

Other books by the same author:

The Hacker Chronicles series
Rebellion
Redemption

FOREWORD

SOME WOULD SAY, HULL, WHERE I hail from, is distinctly a second-division place. And if you're from Grimsby, Scunthorpe, Leeds, Sheffield, or umpteen other nearby places, there's a good chance you might say far worse. As a proud native, I will never agree with any negative viewpoints about my home city. To me, its people, landscapes and blustery North Sea coastline evoke many memories – all of them positive and wholesome. But whatever your perspective, the truth is that by the time the 1970s rolled in, my birthplace had certainly seen more prosperous days. Unemployment was rife after the fishing rights to the North Atlantic had been ceded to Iceland at the end of the bitter 'Cod Wars'. It was a political act that decimated a proud sea-faring heritage in an instant, leaving Hull on its knees economically and many proud East Yorkshire men and women believing they had been betrayed by the national powers that be. To this very day, many remain resentful and will never forgive.

In August 1977, a few short weeks after Queen

Elizabeth's Silver Jubilee festivities had come to a successful conclusion and Hull continued to be enveloped by a financial slump that would last for many years, none of this mattered a jot to me. I had just celebrated my twelfth birthday and, as I had done for the last three years, I was looking forward to the prospect of staying with my beloved Auntie Kathleen and uncles Jim and Fred at their home in Cottingham, where they lived together in harmony.

Auntie Kathleen was born into an old Cottingham family called the Fosters. She was one of several children raised during the years before, and after, the Great War. Emma (my grandma) was the eldest of the brood, Jessie was the middle child, while Kathleen, who had been blessed with a positive outlook on life, was the baby of the bunch. Although they had other siblings, this trio would become inseparable throughout their adult lives.

Uncle Jim was Auntie Kathleen's husband, and Uncle Fred her brother-in-law. They were two men who were bonded by blood, shared experiences and spirit, albeit they had very differing personalities. They came from the Burgess clan, and there had been unhappiness during their early years, so the wider family didn't ask questions that would open up painful wounds. It wasn't a perfect policy – not by modern standards – but it worked for us. Whereas Uncle Jim was quite outgoing, Uncle Fred was a man of few words. If you got "good morning" out of him during a full day, you were doing well. Physically, they looked similar: both were in their fifties, short in stature with receding dark hair and a permanent five o'clock shadow; they always dressed in green or grey Tweed suits (even though one was a bricklayer and the other a labourer), and they would never be seen outside the house without an obligatory flat cap perched on top of their heads. They both cycled to work: Uncle Jim had the shorter distance, riding to Hull and whatever building site the city council dictated he should be at, while Uncle Fred negotiated a thirty-mile round trip every day, as he pedalled all the way to RAF Leconfield and back. But, while they were different in so many ways, the loyalty these brothers had for one another shone through, forged as it had been through the turmoil of the tempestuous 1930s, the ravages of the Second World War, and everything that followed during a protracted period that saw Britain fall from the lofty position it had held in the world for more than two hundred years. During one of the most difficult periods the country has known, they, and Auntie Kathleen, spent more than thirty years creating a home that always offered a hearty welcome and a hot cup of tea. It was a place my mum loved to visit. And I did, too.

Mum and I had left Cottingham in 1974. Until then, we had lived just four doors away from Kathleen, Jim and Fred, sharing a house with my grandad and grandma, whose surname was 'Longbone'. But that year, noted for two general elections, a state of emergency in Northern Ireland and the three-day week, we moved to a small village in Leicestershire. It was a place I quickly grew to dislike; within weeks of arriving, I would be set upon by lads who were often two and three years older than me. My crimes? I had a strong East Yorkshire accent and stood almost a full head and shoulders above my peers, two things that singled me out as being different. Supporting Hull City, a team dubbed by the locals as "crap", only added to my woes. I have since learned that if you speak differently, there is a golden rule: make sure the football team you follow impresses others and gives you some credibility in the playground! City were a struggling Second Division side whose players were deemed unfit to lace the boots of the likes of Frank Worthington, Keith Weller and Jon Samuels, who starred for Leicester City. And because I steadfastly refused to swap allegiances and turn my back on the Tigers, and I spoke a Yorkshire dialect many of the locals struggled to understand, I was often at the centre of trouble not of my making. Thankfully, every year there was a light at the end of the tunnel, for I visited my aunt and uncles so mum could have a couple of weeks of respite during the school holidays. In truth, I also needed to get away. The Leicestershire move had not been a success for mum and had taken its toll; her marriage to my stepfather had ended acrimoniously a few months earlier, leaving her with several emotional mountains to climb. As a result, she suffered from anxiety and depression, and as a single, working mother she needed time to herself to recharge and refocus. Thankfully, she could think of nobody better than Kathleen, Jim and Fred, into whose loving care I was entrusted.

There were many reasons why I enjoyed going to Cottingham, a place I will always think of as 'home', not least the laughter that flowed easily in the scullery and front room of my aunt's modest home in Brockenhurst Avenue, the card games that were often played, the characters who lived close by, and the opportunity to go and support my beloved City. More than anything, however, Auntie Kathleen had a *joie de vivre* that was infectious, and she also spoiled me rotten, making the best cream cakes and trifles I have ever tasted. These were two of the reasons her diabetes, which required three insulin injections every day, could never be brought under control. Another factor was the pan of beef and pork dripping that permanently sat on the gas cooker, providing a delicious accompaniment to the giant doorstep slices of toasted bread that were consumed daily. For Auntie Kathleen, a portly woman who liked to smoke her own roll-ups at least twenty times a day loved nothing more than indulging in life's small pleasures. She would not be denied them, even if doctors insisted she was in mortal danger by refusing to adopt a healthier lifestyle.

"These medical people don't know what they're talking about," she would often say, as she tucked into a seductive slice of homemade Victorian sponge cake and puffed on a cigarette. "I feel fine. And I make sure I eat plenty of fruit every day to compensate for my little extravagances."

With a smile that was never far from her face, my aunt was a woman who was delighted to share good things with those around her. Thankfully, it is a blessing I only visited once a year, for I fear my waist would have grown substantially if I was subjected to the diet imposed on my uncles. Even Sweep the dog, the result of a one-off amorous liaison between a Standard Poodle and a Labrador, was the size of a small outhouse! The truth is, however, happy memories are made by such people, who are natural 'givers' not 'takers'.

That August, many were created – but not all of them strictly for the right reasons… ✳

ONE

Sugar, spice, and all things nice

BOREDOM IS THE CURSE OF all children – and the scourge of their families. And sure enough, despite the best efforts of Auntie Kathleen to keep my mind occupied, shortly after my mum had departed Brockenhurst Avenue to return to Leicestershire, leaving me to enjoy my fort-night-long holiday, I started to become restless.

It was Saturday the thirteenth day of August. The year was 1977, and the start of the football season was a full, excruciating week away. I had been in Cottingham for less than three hours, and as the small arm of the living room clock got nearer to three o'clock – and the booming 'bongs' that hit the same kind of decibel levels as those triggered by Big Ben – I felt an acute bout of mischief start to pulse through my veins. As my poor mother knew only too well, I was often prone to these episodes, hence the need for her to have some time to herself every year.

I looked around at my surroundings. The animated face of Dickie Davies, host of *World of Sport* was speaking on the telly. I couldn't understand what he was talking about as the volume was too low for me to hear anything on the recently acquired Phillips colour 'box'. So, I simply stared at his dark moustache, which bobbed up and down, like a giant leopard moth caterpillar munching its way along a dandelion leaf. Uncle Jim loved to have the telly on as background noise, which meant he could do other things while not missing anything of importance. But I couldn't see the point, particularly as nobody could hear anything. I glanced to my left and my right; Auntie Kathleen had the tip of a black biro pen in her mouth, while Uncle Jim was scratching his ear vigorously with the remnants of a pencil, the type acquired from a local betting shop. Both were totally absorbed by the contents of the *Daily Mirror* and *The Sun* newspapers respectively. It was clear this was their weekend routine; they had settled down to enjoy some peace and quiet and there was nothing (or 'nowt' as they say in these parts) for me to do other than be seen and not heard. I had played with my Airfix toy soldiers for an hour, and the nazi and Japanese axis of evil had lost for the umpteenth time on the stairs and landing to numerically inferior (but militarily superior) British Eighth Army forces. Apart from picking up a book to read, which no self-respecting lad of my age ever did, my options were exhausted. Even Sweep, the resident mutt and the world's worst guard dog, would not be enticed from under the front room table to go for a walk. So, with one of my remaining options being to sit still and be silent (something I could never do), my imagination started to run wild.

Making as little noise as possible, I wandered into the kitchen and spied a bowl of very early season Jaffa oranges. If you haven't tasted the delights of a Jaffa, you have missed a trick: grown in Israel, it is a fruit with the sweetest taste, and in the 1970s, when you could only buy them at certain times of the year, they were more prized than gold bullion (you usually bought them between September and March). I checked to see if anyone was looking – they weren't – so I snaffled two of the largest on offer, tucked them under the Hull City shirt I had been wearing every day for the last two weeks (unwittingly creating the illusion I had started to grow breasts) and meandered into the downstairs bathroom, eager to consume my ill-gotten gains.

"You won't be long, will you?" called Uncle Jim from the comfort of his chair as he eyed the direction in which I was going. "I am starting to get desperate for the loo myself and I know how long you can take in there."

I waved my hand in acknowledgement, never daring to look at him or say a word, lest I slip up, surrender my spoils and incur his wrath. Thankfully, Uncle Jim's eyes quickly settled once again on the inner pages of that day's paper. He was attempting to complete the 'quick' crossword. His endeavours had already eaten up the last forty-five minutes and I knew this latest foolhardy quest would take considerably longer until the white flag of surrender was raised and the newspaper tossed aside. For as long as I could remember, it had been the same outcome every time he attempted the feat. After I had unconsciously eyed the *Mirror's* sordid front page tale about a couple of English school girls who were embroiled in an 'Arab love riddle', I relaxed. Uncle Jim had closed his eyes and was whistling something to himself, and I was as confident as I could be that my small misdemeanour would remain undetected.

Once securely inside the sparse, whitewashed bathroom, comprising a bath, sink and toilet, made some thirty years earlier out of the finest porcelain, I retrieved the two oranges and ate them like a ravenous piranha devours flesh. Boy, they tasted good, despite the overpowering smell of insulin, a drug Auntie Kathleen was required to inject into the fat below her skin every day in a bid to control her diabetes. After the last piece of the fruit had been consumed, and with my fingers dripping in sticky citrus juices, I suddenly realised I had a problem not foreseen when I pocketed these heavenly delights: what would I do with the peel? Throwing it away in the bin was a definite no-no; it was emptied every day and would lead to instant discovery and potentially dire consequences, such as no pudding at the evening meal, as well as certain chastisement from Auntie Kathleen, Uncle Jim, or both. Nor could I flush it down the loo, as the unyielding peel would easily lead to the pipes becoming blocked. So, I had to be clever. Looking around the room, I immediately discounted throwing it out of the small window that overlooked the backyard. That would just be sheer stupidity and lead to quicker discovery than if I had used the bin. Next, I studied the bath panel, which looked like a good spot to hide anything from the incriminating peel to a dead body. Unfortunately, it was secured by screws and I didn't have the means to remove them. It was at that moment I wished I'd bought a Swiss army knife with my birthday money, as well as the Tigers shirt I now wore from dawn to dusk.

Nope, I would be buggered (metaphorically) unless I could find somewhere to dispose of the evidence. And then, just as panic threatened to overwhelm me, I had a light bulb moment. I put the toilet seat down and climbed on top of the lid, so I could reach into the cistern that was located directly above, a good six and a half feet off the ground and way too high to come into Auntie Kathleen and Uncle Jim's direct line of vision. Being taller than the average twelve-year-old, I was able to get my hand into the cold and uninviting water channel. After fumbling around in the depths for a few seconds, I was happy. This would be an ideal spot. I bent down, picked up the peel from the sink, and quietly and surely placed it in the watery hiding place. At a stroke, the evidence of my crime had disappeared. Even the juice that had dripped onto my prized football shirt couldn't be seen as it blended in perfectly with one of the wide amber stripes. Contented, I came out of the toilet and proceeded to let Uncle Jim know it was now 'safe' for him to use.

"That's wonderful," he exhaled, opening his dark brown eyes and talking to me kindly. "But it is usual in these parts for us to flush the toilet when we've used it. Tony, your standards seem to have dropped since you moved to the Midlands. So, can you kindly pull the chain before I go in, there's a good lad and, if it's necessary, open the window."

I looked at his dark, swarthy face (even when he shaved, Uncle Jim's chin looked as though it had not seen a razor blade in weeks) and suddenly the simplest and the most perfect fib popped into my shell-like. "Don't worry Uncle Jim," I said quickly. "I didn't need to go in the end. It was a false alarm."

I must have been convincing, for Uncle Jim seemed satisfied with my response. I hurried away from the scene of the crime, eventually finding myself in the scullery, and feeling the cooling touch of the oilcloth that adorned the table on my leg. As I sat, with my back to the front room, I heard my uncle rise from his seat, grumble at the outcome of the latest race from Haydock Park, which presumably meant he had lost a couple of bob on the result, and stride purposefully to the loo. I remained still, not moving until I heard the door close and the latch drop. I sighed as an immense feeling of relief washed over me.

Looking around, I marvelled at all the freshly baked foods on display. A chocolate sponge cake caught my attention immediately. It was filled with strawberry jam and fresh cream, which had spilt over the sides. It sat invitingly on a plate on the wooden shelf of the main cupboard, drawing me towards it like a magnet pulls in an iron filing. It took all my self-control to stop myself from flicking my finger across the rich seams of jam and cream. I licked my lips, anticipating the joys to come later in the day. There were also scones aplenty (the ones with raisins in them) and a meat pie. Then I eyed some fish fillets; they appeared to be smoked haddock, as the flesh was a yellowish colour. There were also some large pieces of plaice, which were Auntie Kathleen's favourites. Their tails poked out of the plain white paper they had been wrapped in, a sure sign Mister Wigby, the man who sold groceries and meats from his mobile van to the residents of Brockenhurst Avenue at least twice a week, had been in the vicinity. When I had clocked everything that was on offer, I leaned to the side, stretched out my right arm, and gently eased open the bright white pantry door. Inside this particular Aladdin's Cave were a large chicken, some dairy items and tinned foods, including enough corned beef to feed the British army. I smiled. It looked like we would be feasting over the next few days in the truest of Auntie

Kathleen traditions. But the prospect of a meal, or two, wasn't enough. I remained restless. I still wasn't contented and my boredom was increasing. I tried to fight the urges from within but was unable to resist. And from that moment, there was only one possible outcome: I was going to be in a spot of bother.

As is often the case, it was at that precise moment I spotted an intriguing glass bowl. Made to withstand heavy knocks and blows, it looked as though it must have been manufactured before Uncle Jim enlisted with the East Yorkshire Infantry to go and fight in the Second World War, a good thirty-six years earlier. But what particularly caught my attention was the little mountain of sugar it contained! Now then, I thought, there's something...

I had always wanted to trick someone into using salt instead of sugar. I think I had first seen such a prank being played out when I watched an old black and white film one Saturday morning on the BBC. The thought you could hoodwink someone so simply, with such devastating effect, made it all the more appealing. Thereafter I'd always wanted to recreate a similar kind of chaos. So today, just a few hours into my stay, I decided Uncle Jim, one of my favourite people in the whole world, was going to be my unsuspecting victim.

"Auntie Kathleen," I called out using all my charm while trying my hardest to stifle an involuntary chuckle that was threatening to escape. "Would you and Uncle Jim like me to make you both a nice cup of coffee?"

Prior to posing the question, I'd already placed two cups alongside the cooker and got an unopened bottle of 'steri' (sterilised milk) out of the fridge (prising its metal lid off with a bottle opener), and I'd filled the metal kettle with water and placed it on the lit cooker ring. All of these things had been done before I heard Auntie Kathleen's confirmatory "yes, please", which meant the plot was now entering its decisive phase. I looked over my shoulder in the direction of the downstairs toilet – a place I hoped would continue to be Uncle Jim's home for a few minutes longer. All continued to be quiet; there was nothing to suggest he might be ready to return to his place by the fire and telly. The only sound was a light, occasional cough, which indicated he was still trying to overcome the disappointment of his latest crossword failure, as well as attending to nature's call.

As the kettle's liquid contents noisily bubbled and hissed away, I peered into the pantry in an effort to try and locate the all-important salt. Sure enough, I quickly spotted a packet of Saxa, which had barely been used. Its extrovert gold, white and blue packaging made it easy to identify. I reached for it, grabbed hold and eased it out of its resting place. Once everything I needed was at my fingertips, I hastily poured the sugar out of the bowl, onto a plate, which I hid on one of the shelves in the pantry. Then I started the most important part of the grand deception... the swap! It only took a few, fleeting seconds to complete the task, and when it looked as though the salt equalled the amount of displaced sugar, my wicked sense of humour was well on the way to being sated. But just as smugness threatened to overwhelm me, the peace of the house was shattered.

"What in buggery's name is wrong with this damned toilet?" I heard Uncle Jim shout behind the solid white screen of the lavatory door. At the same time came the sound of the toilet chain being repeatedly yanked followed by the cistern emitting strangled gurgling noises. At my tender time of life, I knew nothing about plumbing, but it was abundantly clear that number thirteen's loo did not want to comply with the wishes of the flusher.

"Damn you. Damn you. Damn you," my normally softly-spoken uncle roared in frustration, as his efforts failed to bear fruit. "Bugger. I suppose I will just have to bloody well sort this out. Whatever could be wrong with the damned thing?"

Suddenly, the cistern fell silent, albeit movement and what sounded like some physical exertion continued – the result, I suspect, of trousers being pulled up and a belt being buckled. Auntie Kathleen stirred in her chair momentarily, looking in the direction of the scullery, before an article about the rock singer, Freddie Mercury, penned by Nina Myskow in *The Sun*, reclaimed her attention. She continued to be focused on the newspaper while splashes and grunts, the results of Uncle Jim's urgent investigations, shattered the hitherto peace and calm. At first, I couldn't fathom what was going on. And then the penny dropped: as I had done earlier, Uncle Jim had climbed onto the toilet seat, perched on his tip-toes, and was attempting to discover the source of the blockage. It was then that my heart started thumping wildly.

Time was of the essence. After pouring water and milk into both cups, I quickly took the coffees into the sitting room, placing them on the small trestle tables located by the sides of the chairs Auntie Kathleen and Uncle Jim claimed as their own. As she received my offering, Auntie Kathleen made an approving cooing noise. Her eyes never shifted from the columns of the newspaper, such were her powers of coordination, and quickly the combination of warm drink and exaggerated newspaper stories consumed her. I had also taken the sugar bowl with me, so Uncle Jim could access its contents. I placed it on the table by his cup. I had almost managed to make it back to the relative safety of the scullery table when I heard him exclaim: "What in hell is this doing in here?" Less than thirty seconds later, he emerged from the toilet. "Young man," he bellowed in my general direction. "I think you have some explaining to do."

As I turned and faced my accuser, I saw the shirt sleeve cuffs on his right arm were wet through, while his hand was gripping all that remained of the two succulent Jaffas. But before I could say anything in my defence, Uncle Jim spied the cup of steaming coffee by his chair. Like the captain of a Seventeenth Century galleon being guided onto the rocks by the mesmerising calls of a mermaid seductress, the lure of a cup of Nescafe proved too great a temptation. My conscience suddenly sparked to life and I tried to warn him of the imminent danger he faced. Nervous, I stammered incoherently, but my words were immediately cut off.

"Hold on to your thoughts, Tony," said Uncle Jim, stopping me in my tracks. "You can think about your answer, and how you will atone after I have drunk my coffee. After buggering about in the toilet, sorting out the mess only you could have created, I am now in need of some refreshment."

With that, Uncle Jim proceeded to launch a teaspoon into the sugar bowl. Once, twice. thrice, four times… depositing what he thought were pyramids of the finest British cane sugar into the piping hot liquid. Then, in a bid to make the coffee more temperate, he blew short blasts of air across its surface, creating little ripples akin to rolling waves gently caressing the seashore. Only when he was satisfied he wouldn't scald his mouth did he take an almighty swig. And that was his downfall.

Time seemed to stand still for a moment before I became aware of Uncle Jim's swarthy face turning crimson red, his eyes bulging then narrowing into slits before an involuntary percussive explosion erupted from his mouth as he violently expelled the foul-tasting and invasive brown liquid. It was as if Iceland's famous Strokkur geyser had transported itself momentarily into number thirteen, for the scale of the plume that spurted from his mouth that day (soaking the wall, opposite) certainly had supernatural qualities. Very quickly, my uncle's confusion turned to bewilderment, followed by shock, anger and then gradual realisation. Joey, the resident and normally anonymous house budgie who lived permanently in the front room, started hopping from one perch to another in his small wiry cage, making wild and raucous hooting noises as he expressed his mirth at the scene being played out before him. His squawks added to the overall pandemonium and helped to rouse the normally docile Sweep, who started barking energetically, his tail thumping rhythmically against the brown, dralon settee. Amid this scene of utter bedlam, Uncle Jim was rapidly regaining his senses. When he had done so, he caught my eye. And it was at that very moment, I realised he was capable of being a cold-blooded killer. He had, after all, fought in Burma against the formidable Japanese.

"You conniving little devil," he ranted, as he rose from his chair. "When I get my hands on you I am going to bloody well flay you alive." The next thing I knew was

Uncle Jim had hurled himself out of his chair and in my general direction. Thankfully, I had my wits about me and was prepared. I legged it as quickly as I could, making for the back door and the freedom of the yard outside. If I could escape the confines of the house, there was a fighting chance Auntie Kathleen would intervene and I would be safe.

"Come here, you little monkey," I heard Uncle Jim rasp, as I reached for the door handle and twisted the knob, allowing the wooden obstruction to swing open and my legs to propel me into the fresh air. Then, my prayers were indeed answered: Auntie Kathleen had decided she needed to sort things out.

"Jim! Jim! Calm down," she said soothingly in her distinctive and softly spoken East Yorkshire voice. She folded her arms and looked at us both as she stood on the outside steps by the back door, having glided their effortlessly from the comfort of her chair. Unlike her husband, she was the picture of serenity. "Whatever has happened, remember he's only a young lad, and he's only playing the kind of prank you would have been proud of when you were his age. There's no serious harm done."

Uncle Jim disagreed and continued to spit barbs in my direction. "No harm? I nearly choked on that vile stuff," he said as he joined his wife on the steps and started mopping the sweat off his brow with a handkerchief. "It feels like I've drunk half the bloody Humber estuary. And then there's the matter of the orange peel I found in the cistern. He's only just arrived, and already we've got havoc raining down on us. I am not having it, Kathleen. I am not having it. Tony is going to have to buck his ideas up if he going to last the fortnight."

"Oh, Jim, don't get yourself all worked up," urged my aunt, a woman who would have made a wonderful diplomat if she had been blessed with an education and a more fortunate upbringing. "Look on the bright side, it got you out of that chair you had been slumped in for half the day. And there's no lasting harm done. Anyway, what did he actually do to cause such a commotion? What real harm is there?"

Uncle Jim put his hand on Auntie Kathleen's shoulder, turned her around so she was facing the front room, and pointed his finger directly at the sugar bowl.

"Take a look for yourself," he urged. "Go and taste what's in that bowl. Just make sure you don't swallow too much of it."

With curiosity written all over her face, Auntie Kathleen strode purposefully to the crime scene, licked her index finger and dipped it into the sugar bowl. I should have warned her beforehand not to do it. But before my brain had clicked into gear, her finger had disappeared into her mouth. It was an act she regretted instantly. Her cheeks imploded, and a gagging noise, the sort made by a Baboon when it is the height of the mating season, came out of her mouth. Moving at a speed that belied her age and weight, my aunt made for the scullery sink, where she turned on the cold tap, allowing a torrent to blast the sides of the stainless steel sink. She quickly cupped one of her hands, capturing some of the outpouring in her palm, and proceeded to gulp down the comforting water. Eventually, when the foul taste had subsided, she had composed herself, and the twinkle had returned to her eye, she looked at me and said: "If your mum finds out about this, she'll give you a good hiding, and it will be nothing more than you deserve. And if you try anything else like this while you are here, you won't be able to sit down for a week because I will sort you out myself. And I promise it will be a painful experience."

Then, with her words hanging in the air but unable to contain herself, Auntie Kathleen let out one of her signature belly laughs. "So, are we agreed?" she asked while trying her best to conceal the sniggers that overwhelmed any feelings of anger. "You're going to be on your best behaviour for the rest of your stay, aren't you?"

I nodded my assent, eager to please the woman who was the beloved matriarch figure of our family. And at that precise moment, I meant it: I was willing to be compliant, the good nephew who never knowingly put a foot wrong. Alas, as anyone who has passed through childhood will know, two weeks is a very long time for any young lad to remember all the solemn pledges they have made.

I was, therefore, doomed to fail. ✳

PHILIP YORKE

TWO

The great lemonade bottle swindle

INGLEMIRE LANE RUNS FROM HULL ROAD (in Cottingham), all the way down to Beverley Road (in Hull). It passes the site of the old Jackson's meat processing plant, scores of pre-war houses, and at least one of the city's very best fish and chip shops. It also extended itself beyond a plot of land owned by the University of Hull, where John Kaye's Tigers were busily preparing themselves to meet Sunderland in the opening Division Two league encounter at Boothferry Park at the end of the week.

As well as being a long thoroughfare, 'the Lane' was also home to one of my favourite shops. George and Nora Elliott had owned their popular newsagents for seven years. Family friends and neighbours who also lived in Brockenhurst Avenue, were regulars, as were Uncle Jim and Uncle Fred, who popped in daily to buy their packets of Embassy No 6 King Size on their way back from work. I was known to them. And so, too, was mum. I was always polite to the Elliotts whenever I bought my packets of sweets (usually Sherbet Dips and Liquorice Allsorts), and

24

they were friendly and encouraging whenever they took the pennies I offered up in payment.

As well as visiting the shop for my own needs, Auntie Kathleen would often ask me to go and fetch her Old Holborn tobacco from the Elliotts. It was a ten-minute round trip that frequently allowed me to buy fizzy drinks that came in glass bottles. In those impoverished days, glass had a real value, and there was a drive to recycle as much of it as possible. So, for every large empty bottle that was returned to the Elliotts, a refund of two pence would be made to the lucky soul who claimed their reward. Best of all, no proof of purchase was ever required to claim the cash.

When I was twelve, I had never heard of the word 'entrepreneur'. To be honest, I knew nothing about the business world and rarely watched the news on the box, and I had never really been exposed to big words like this. Mum and I never talked of these things, and neither did my family. Fast forward more than four decades and using this very word can be akin to calling someone a criminal. The only difference is an entrepreneur usually gets away with things while a common thief doesn't. And on the fifteenth day of the month (a Monday), as I sat eating a bowl of cornflakes in Auntie Kathleen's scullery and she stood by the ancient mangle, putting her freshly laundered washing through it, a cunning plan popped into my young mind that was very *entrepreneurial*. I wasn't specifically thinking about doing something wrong. The thought just popped into my head and I couldn't get rid of it. But for it to work, I needed to recruit some help. Thankfully, growing up in Cottingham meant I knew some of the local children and continued to play with them whenever I returned to these parts. I was confident, once I had spoken to Shaun Goadby and the Sidebottom boys (Paul and Ian), who both lived next door to one another on the Lane, there would be four of us itching to take part in an audacious mission that had every chance of netting us a tidy sum. So, I asked Auntie Kathleen if I could go out and visit some old friends, without specifically naming who I was going to see. It was a request to which she happily agreed.

I met my fellow co-conspirators at eleven o'clock in the morning after I had tempted them to leave their back gardens with the promise of untold riches. Unsure why I had dragged them away from a game of Scrabble and reading *The Lion, The Witch and The Wardrobe*, I quickly explained my intentions as we convened by a tall privet hedge less than two hundred yards away from Elliotts. Before revealing my hand, I was unsure how the proposal would be received, for there was every chance I would be told to bugger off. But that wasn't their reaction. Far from it.

"So, tell us again," said Paul after I had explained the perfect, victimless crime to him and the others. "Who is doing what, and are you really sure it's going to be that easy?"

A year and a half older than me, Paul had a haircut that made him look like one of the cartoon characters in the Homepride Flour adverts that regularly appeared in newspapers and on the box. I had known him and his two brothers for as long as I could remember, but he didn't like me that much. At best, he tolerated me – particularly on the occasions I said or did something that piqued his interest. And that day, I had certainly got his full attention. On other occasions, he would completely ignore me, or give me a thump on the shoulder that usually left me with a dead arm.

"What don't you understand?" I replied, sounding a little bit too defensive. "It's easy-peasy, and the simplest way you'll ever make some money."

Ian, Paul's brother who was the same age as me, sided with his older sibling. "Just tell us again how we are not going to get caught, or into trouble?" he urged. "It's that bit that frightens me the most. Our mum and dad will kill us if they ever find out."

I looked at them all. Paul and Ian stared directly at me, awaiting my reply. Only Shaun, a blonde-haired youth who was half my size, wouldn't engage in eye contact. He kept his focus firmly on the pavement, an action I have since come to realise is a clear signal someone thinks a scheme hasn't got a cat in hell's chance of working. But rather than confess his doubts there and then, Shaun just continued to stare downwards while pushing a pebble around with his right foot, as if he were Cottingham's equivalent of George Best.

"It's dead simple," I said. "At the side of Elliotts, there is an area where they store all their glass pop bottles. There are loads of them and I doubt whether they ever get checked. They will never notice if we sneak into their back-yard and take a few from the pile, and then go inside and claim the money. I reckon if we take three at a time, say every fifteen minutes, within an hour we'll have got enough cash to buy a load of sweets. Each of us will have to have a go. But the risk is absolute zero. And the Elliotts will never know what we have done."

Paul's eyes narrowed. There was clearly something agitating him. "And how do we get into the backyard?" he inquired. "There is no way the gate will be left open, and even if it was, they would definitely hear us."

Triumphantly, I proceeded to unveil how we could remain undetected for the duration of the heist – and how an ancient house, which was home to an old lady who belonged to the Quakers (and where religious meetings were regularly held) was an integral part of the plot.

"We can use the old lady's garden to shield us," I told him. "It goes all the way up to the yard where the bottles are kept. Since yesterday, I have checked it out several times. It will be a doddle. All we have to do is get into the garden unseen and then get to the barbed wire fence. Once we're there, we'll be able to see everything that's going on and make sure Mr and Mrs Elliott aren't around. When the coast is clear, we'll climb over the fence, take the bottles, and start claiming our reward. I'll go first. Paul will go second, and then it's Ian. You'll go last, Shaun."

I mentioned Shaun's name more loudly than the others in a bid to shake him out of his state of disinterest. It did the trick: he nearly jumped out of his skin. "Okay," he said. "There's no need to shout. I more than get it. I am the last one to go and, as you've said, everything will be fine." Despite his reassurances, Shaun didn't sound convinced. And although he said he was willing to participate, his coolness forced me to have doubts for the first time. I started to ponder the plan's merits, not realising I had wandered off into a daydream. I was brought back into reality when Paul hit my shoulder and I felt yet another dull ache take hold of my arm. His punch also signalled it was time to get going.

Thankfully, the Lane is long and straight, so you have good visibility when looking left and right. And as we made our descent into the old lady's garden, successfully squeezing past the tall pillars that held two large gates in place, there were no cars or lorries in sight. Nor were there any pedestrians about. Apart from a bedroom curtain opening, and then shutting again rather quickly in a house opposite, there was nothing for us to be remotely concerned about. It really did seem as though our luck was riding high that particular morning.

Once we were on the other side, and safely concealed from prying eyes, we began the process of skirting the extensive garden's perimeter, where a ditch no more than three feet deep conveniently led all the way to the newsagent's backyard. Carefully, the four of us made our way through bracken and the broken branches of an assortment of mature trees. We also did our best to dodge the thorns of protective bramble bushes doing their best to impede our progress. As I heard the distinctive crack of a branch, a sure sign some careless soul had trodden on it, I also heard the tell-tale sound of muffled cries of pain. I looked around and saw Ian and Shaun wiping blood off their cheeks simultaneously after they strayed too close to a particularly vindictive mass of leaves, thorns and tempting brambles, which, when they were close enough, lashed out and punctured their skin. The assault wasn't quite on the scale, or violence, associated with the fates that befell the National Guardsmen in the film *Southern Comfort*, but the scene was certainly reminiscent of coming under attack from unseen assassins. At that moment, I found myself thanking our lucky stars that we weren't required to go too far under such conditions, as I fear we would never have made our ultimate destination – the back of the old coal shed.

With all four of us squatting behind the brickwork of the outbuilding, I took it upon myself to lift my head above the parapet and discover if our movements had remained undetected. Pushing upwards, I gradually increased my height, holding on to the mossy bricks as I rose from the bowels of the ditch, and soon, with only my forehead and eyes revealed, I could see everything that was happening in the yard, and via a small window, I could also make out what appeared to be a storage area at the back of the shop. A shiver ran down my spine as I sized up the riches that awaited.

"There are hundreds of bottles," I said in a hushed voice while trying desperately to contain my excitement. "There's going to be loads to choose from. And best of all, I can't see anyone. It all looks good to me."

With that, the Sidebottom boys and Shaun all hauled themselves up and adopted the same stance I had taken. After a while, presumably while surveying the same inactive scene before admitting it was safe to proceed, they nodded in agreement and visibly relaxed. It was time for me to carry out the first excursion, thereby proving the next phase of the plan would also work. I edged closer to the barbed wire, taking time to look around and get my bearings and ensure nobody was lurking in the shadows waiting to pounce. After carrying out a thorough risk assessment (which involved staring left, right and centre for thirty seconds), I took a deep breath and straddled the wire, which was only about three feet in height. It was an easy obstacle to overcome and, in the blink of an eye, I found I had made it into the backyard of Elliotts. I quickly took stock of the bottles. Directly in front of me were crates of Corona lemonade bottles, all with their distinctive white labels and bright yellow lettering. To the left was the space allocated to Orangeade and Limeade, while to the right there were neatly stacked rows of empty Cherryade, Dandelion and

Burdock and Cream Soda. I felt overwhelmed. It felt like I had entered *the* Aladdin's Cave of the soft drinks world. I quickly grabbed the first empty three bottles I could lay my hands on, put them under my armpit, and then hastily negotiated the barbed wire as I retreated to the safety of the brickwork.

"That was simple enough," said Paul when I returned unscathed. "But I am not going anywhere near those bottles until you have been into the shop and got the money." I suspected the three of them had been conferring while I set about securing the ill-gotten spoils because Ian and Shaun both made murmuring noises that sounded vaguely supportive of the declaration.

"No problem," I said. "Wish me luck."

With that, I retraced my steps back to the large gate, ever mindful of the vicious nature of the bramble bush that had already drawn blood from two members of the gang, and squeezed through the small gap. As I re-emerged, a startled pigeon took off from an overhanging branch of a Sycamore Tree. As I looked up and watch it flee the scene, I noticed the curtain-twitching once again in the house opposite. I couldn't see anyone, so I carried on about my business and within sixty seconds I was standing before Mrs Elliott – Norah to her friends – having placed my three empties on her counter.

"Have we been having a party at your aunt's?" she enquired jovially as she made her way to the till. "That's an awful lot of lemonade to be putting away. I hope you have been brushing your teeth well at night, otherwise all that sugar will damage your teeth?"

Without waiting for my reply, Mrs Elliott pressed a couple of the keys, a bell rang, the till opened noisily and the sound of pennies being toyed with filled the air.

"Hold out your hand," Mrs Elliott said after she had finished examining the till. I immediately did as I was told, and my fingers strained eagerly as they sought to clutch the coins. "One. Two. Three. Four. Five. And six. That's your lot," she said, pointing in the direction of the shelves that held the massed ranks of the glass jars containing the multi-coloured sweets. "Now, is there anything you'd like to buy with that little collection, or are you simply going to be on your way home?"

Unable to speak due to my surprise at the ease with which my plan had worked, I simply smiled at the friendly and trusting newsagent, raised my hand nervously to signal I was leaving and set about getting out of the shop as quickly as my legs would take me. In truth, I was bricking it and had I spoken, Mrs Elliott would have known I was up to something. But as the front door to Elliotts closed behind me, I felt sheer joy as the six pennies jangled against one another in my pocket as I raced back to the hideaway, where the rest were waiting.

"It worked. It really worked," said an excited Paul, as I retrieved the coins from my pocket and showed the delighted trio. "I never believed you would get away with it. But you did. You flipping well did."

I smiled. Coming from Paul, this was praise indeed. "Let's give it ten minutes, and then it's your turn," I whispered to him. "Best to keep going, eh?"

Then we froze. The distinctive noise of footsteps on concrete that were too close for comfort snapped us out of our congratulatory mood. There was an energy to them that was a little unnerving, and there was a degree of urgency. Suddenly they stopped. But the person was definitely close by, because no sooner had silence descended than the gate to the backyard started to shake as its handle was twisted violently, first one way, then the other. Thankfully, it held firm. It was securely locked. Whoever was trying to get in would have to try another way. As if thinking the same thing, we heard footsteps once again, this time, however, they were walking away from the yard.

"For a moment, I thought our luck had run out," I said feeling relieved. "It sounded like somebody knew something wasn't quite right and was investigating."

A nervous ripple of laughter cascaded among us, the way it does when boys are nervous but are too afraid to admit it. It lasted only a few seconds before it petered out. If we had been born with any sense at all, we would have settled for a net gain of six pennies. But we were far from sensible. So, when we considered a suitable amount of time had lapsed, Paul rose from the ditch, clambered over the barbed wire and continued with the business of collecting empties and relieving the Elliotts of their hard-earned cash. And everything proceeded as planned: Paul took his collection of bottles to Mrs Elliott and was rewarded with a further six pennies; a further fifteen minutes later, Ian did likewise. If anything, his was the smoothest transaction of the lot, taking considerably less time to complete than the previous two. The omens continued to look good.

Last up was Shaun. From the moment he got to his feet, I sensed there would be trouble "Can't we just leave with eighteen pennies, and be happy with that?" he pleaded. "I don't feel good and I really don't want to do this."

Before I could respond, Paul had lent over and was attempting to put some fire in young Shaun's belly. "There is nothing to be scared about," he told his friend. "They are not suspicious at all. But if you prefer to do things a bit differently, then do so. Why not just take a couple of bottles into the shop, that way the Elliotts really won't suspect a thing?"

Immediately, Shaun looked revitalised. There is no way anything I could have said would have had a similar impact. But because Paul had spoken, Shaun had set aside his misgivings. At last, he was up for it. "Okay," he said. "Wish me luck." And before we could respond, he was on his way.

Shaun almost hurdled the barbed wire, such was his haste to hunt down his quota of bottles. And before we could blink, he had picked up three empty Cherryades and was quickly into his stride on the return leg, again forcing his short legs to leap the barrier in a style reminiscent of the great American athlete, Edwin Moses. I'd be surprised if the whole exercise had taken more than sixty seconds, such was the speed at which it was conducted. Now there was only Mrs Elliott to deal with for us to get our hands on the final installment of cash. Shaun didn't hold back in this regard, and we didn't need to look to learn of his progress, as he crashed, banged and walloped his way through the garden undergrowth, again coming a cropper at the bramble bush. But he refused to be knocked out of his stride, so we quickly heard the rhythmic pounding of training shoes as he ran from the gate to the shop front. He drew breath at the door, before opening it and entering. And then he was in – and we waited. By the time five minutes had lapsed, all three of us were getting agitated. Then we heard mysterious footsteps once again. They grew louder and louder until they, too, arrived at the front door of Elliotts. The clang of the doorbell signalled their owner had entered the shop.

Hoping and praying, we all craned our necks willing Shaun to be travelling in the opposite direction. There was no such luck, and the silence suddenly became overpowering.

"I think we need to leave right now," said Ian, who was growing more nervous by the minute. "Something has gone wrong, so we have got to get away as quickly as possible. If we don't, we're going to get caught and into loads of trouble."

"I agree," said Paul. "We are going to find ourselves in the smelly stuff if we stay here."

All three of us rose at the same time, our only thought being self-preservation. But just as we were about to depart, the back door of the shop opened and the familiar figure of Mr Elliott – or 'Gordon' as he was known to uncles Jim and Fred – emerged into the sunlight, and he strode over to where we were hiding. He said: "Okay, you three. The game's up. You have been caught red-handed. Now get out of that garden, which you have no right to be in, and get into the front of my shop so myself and Mrs Elliott can tell you what is going to happen next."

Ashen-faced and in a state of shock, myself, Paul and Ian did as we had been instructed, walking solemnly and tormenting ourselves as we played out the likely scenarios in our heads, most of which featured getting a severe punishment. By the time we got to the glass-fronted door, with its cheery Walls Ice Cream sign beckoning us in, we feared the worst. We trooped into the small shop so meekly you could hear the squeaks of the soles of our training shoes as they made contact with the tiled floor. Shaun was at the end of the shop, where he was sitting on a chair. He was holding his hands, looked frightened and had clearly been crying. Standing next to him was a man wearing a smart suit. I didn't recognise him, but Paul did and he immediately cursed under his breath.

"We are in serious trouble," he hissed. "That's only Bob Starkey, the copper. He and his wife are friends with my mum and dad, and they are going to really give us a walloping when we get home. I wish I had never listened to your crazy plan."

As I mulled over Paul's barb, Mr Elliott rapped the counter with a wooden ruler. In unison, we all looked up and must have appeared quite pathetic. "You really have surpassed yourselves today, haven't you?" he said in a staccato and unemotional voice. "A right little nest of thieves aren't you? Cottingham's very own Al Capones." Mr Elliott let his words hang in the air, drawing the maximum effect. "So, we have caught you in the act stealing from us. But my question goes beyond today because I want to know how much more have you taken from this shop over the past few weeks, eh? Are you the ones who have been responsible for all the shoplifting Mrs Elliott and I have suffered during the summer, I wonder?"

Ian and Paul glanced at one another, and before I realised what was going on, they said with one voice: "It was all his idea, Mr Elliott. He's to blame." As they made this declaration, Paul's finger pointed accusingly in my direction.

"Is that so?" enquired the newsagent as he proceeded to manoeuvre himself behind us, blocking off any thoughts we may have had of making a desperate dash for freedom. "Well, I am not sure what to believe. For all I know, we may have caught a load of young gangsters who are responsible for all the major crimes in this area, isn't that right Bob?"

At the mention of his name, Bob Starkey moved forward a pace. He had been lurking in the shadows and was a giant of a man, standing at least six and a half feet tall, and looking as though he could challenge Muhammad Ali for the world heavyweight boxing title – and possibly win. A member of the local CID, he was certainly not a man you messed with. Yet when he spoke, I almost sniggered out loud. "Vat's abs-holutely correct, Misht-her Elliott," he said, doing everything he could to conceal a pronounced speech impediment. "I may have to take you down to the police stay-shun right now, charge you with this ker-yme, and others, and lock you in the cells. And I will do so if you don't ansh-her our quest-shuns honestly. Is that something vat would make your parents pw-owd of you?"

It was too much for Shaun to take. He started blubbing and was quickly followed by Ian, whose sobs bounced off the wall.

"Paul's right," I said, hoping I could placate the Elliotts and bring proceedings to a quick and decisive end. "This was all my idea. I am the one to blame, and I am very sorry for what we have done. I didn't realise it was seriously wrong; I just thought it was a way for us to be able to get some sweets. That's all, honest. I have only been in Cottingham for just over a day, so you can't accuse me of stealing anything else. And there is no way Paul, Ian and Shaun would ever come in here and steal from you, Mr Elliott. That's the absolute truth."

Gordon Elliott eyed me for what seemed an eternity. His mouth remained thin-lipped, but I could see his eyes, shielded by his heavily framed spectacles, were carefully appraising me, working out whether he could believe me, or not. After a few seconds, he had made up his mind. Pointing at Paul, Ian and Shaun, he said: "You three, off you go. Get home and make sure you tell your mums and dads what you have done. If they decide to give you the good hidings you deserve, then understand that is a small price for what you have done today. Now, be away with you."

With Mr Elliott's words hanging in the air, my accomplices darted through the shop, into the midday sunshine that greeted them, running as fast as their legs would take them. Bob Starkey also chose this moment to leave the scene of the crime.

"If you are you o-o-o-kay tidying f-ings up here, G-G-Gordon?" he stammered. "I will get b-b-b-ack home. It's been a long week already, and it's only flipping M-m-m-m-o-n-day!" He closed the front door behind him, and as the bell signalled his departure Mrs Elliott, who I always thought was a formidable lady, emerged from nowhere. But instead of looking angry, her face appeared to be full of concern. "Whatever were you thinking of, Tony?" she asked. "Haven't we known you for years, ever since you were just out of your nappy? What are you doing taking from us, from people who are friends with your mum, and your aunt and uncles? It's a funny way to repay the kindness we have shown your family, don't you think?"

I was lost for words. I didn't know what to say.

"Now, you listen to me," continued Mrs Elliott. "You and the others should be in serious trouble for what you have tried to get away with today. But we, Mr Elliott and myself are going to give you a second chance. If you promise not to try and con us again, we will put this whole matter behind us. But you have to promise, and you have to mean it. Do you think you can do that?"

I nodded, still dumbstruck by her words.

"Good," she said. "I am delighted that's how you feel.

We know you're not a bad lad, and neither are the other boys. But stealing just the smallest of things can lead to all sorts of troubles further down the line, and it wouldn't be right to let you off without any punishment whatsoever. So this time tomorrow, you'll come back here and you will help to load all those bottles from the backyard onto the back of the Corona lorry that's going to take them away, to be reused. Do I have your word you will be here at twelve o'clock sharp?"

I looked Mrs Elliott directly in the eye, feeling nothing other than admiration and respect for her.. "I promise I will be here," I said. "I am really sorry for what I have done."

The Elliotts looked at one another, seemingly happy. Then Mrs Elliott abruptly piped up: "I think we'll be relieving you of the bottle money you took from us earlier. Hand them over; let's be having those coins back, Tony."

I did as I was told, and as soon as the money had been returned to the to the till, I was allowed to leave. In a bid to retain as much dignity as possible, I casually walked backwards on the tiled floor.. Unfortunately, I failed to see a protruding tile until it was far too late. I collapsed in a heap on the floor, much to the amusement of the Elliotts.

"You wouldn't be old enough to appreciate what I am about to say to you, Tony," said Mrs Elliott between bursts of laughter. "But what you have just experienced is what we adults call 'the consequences of your actions'. Now get up, dust yourself down and be on your way. We expect to see you again at midday tomorrow, no sooner, and no later."

And with that, I had my liberty once again – to reflect and thank my lucky stars. ✳

THREE

The king is dead

ROCK AND ROLL IS A music genre I have never cared for. My mum loved it, particularly the rebellious stuff from the 1950s. And one man, more than any other, was her idol – Elvis Presley, the singer dubbed 'The King' by fans, commentators and all and sundry whenever the subject of who the world's greatest popular singer was.

To me, a young pup who had no musical knowledge whatsoever, he was just a smooth-looking bloke with a huge mass of black hair, who was always on the television, singing soppy songs while wiggling his hips and doing contortions with his legs that were unnatural. I didn't like watching him on the box and always tried to switch to another channel when he came on (if mum wasn't in the vicinity). I also did the same whenever he came on Radio One. I am not sure why I took an instant dislike to the man. But I did.

For mum, Elvis could do no wrong. He was the superstar who changed everything for her generation, doing so much to alter the face of popular music. For after the end of the war, big bands were still in vogue, as were crooners like Nat King Cole, Perry Como and Harry Belafonte. But none of them could quite capture the mood of the day. Their music wasn't innovative, it wasn't exciting, and it had no soul – unlike Elvis's songs, which were heavily charged with electricity and carefully crafted to get the heart beating and feet tapping. And more than twenty years after he first created pandemonium among women of all ages, his formula was still resonating with millions of people around the world.

Mum and I had set out just after breakfast and travelled the hundred and twenty miles from Leicestershire to Hull in her second-hand, blue Renault 4 car, which, to be honest, had seen better days. It was battered in one or two places, felt like you were sailing on a rough sea when you went around a corner, and was just an embarrassing vehicle to be seen in for any self-respecting youngster whose ambitions were more in line with Ford Capris than knackered French vehicles. Mum wasn't always happy with her car either, not least because it occasionally broke down. But despite its faults, it did have one redeeming feature: the cassette player that belted out loud music. So, when mum and I spent just over three hours driving up the A46, A1 and the A63 to East Yorkshire, guess who we listened to all the way? Yep, 'The King'! By the time we turned into Brockenhurst Avenue, and Auntie Kathleen's house was within touching distance, I was desperate to get out of the car. I never wanted to hear an Elvis song again after being subjected to *Jailhouse Rock*, *Love Me Tender*, *Return to Sender* and *Always On My Mind* more times than I care to remember. I knew every word. And even worse than that, I found myself humming these tunes and singing the lyrics.

When mum departed Cottingham, to return home, I prayed Elvis might be forgotten for a couple of weeks, for my aunt and uncles were not fans of rock and roll. They could stomach crooners like Val Doonican and Des O'Connor, but that was their limit. They much preferred to watch TV programmes like *Coronation Street*, *Dad's Army*, *Morecambe and Wise*, *The Two Ronnies* and *Mike Yarwood*. Coincidentally, at least four of these were my favourites too.

At least for a couple of days, as I unsuccessfully set about not getting into trouble, all talk and thoughts of Elvis were banished. Then we arrived on the sixteenth day of August – a Tuesday…

I awoke in an agitated state. I had gone to sleep fearing Mr and Mrs Elliott may change their minds about giving me a second chance and make a surprise (and very unwelcome) visit to Auntie Kathleen's to tell her, and Uncle Jim, about my criminal activity. So, unable to sleep much after seven o'clock in the morning, I went downstairs, opened the sitting room curtains and watched the comings and goings of neighbours like a hawk. I was surprised to hear Auntie Kathleen already awake and at work: she was in the scullery, doing some washing and baking. Such was my anxiety, I stretched every ligament and sinew in my body to be able to see as much as I could. Occasionally, I relaxed and moved to the chair, where Auntie Kathleen tackled her crossword puzzles every day. But whenever I heard movement on the pavement outside, I rushed to the front window to see if my worst fears were about to be realised. After worrying about what was going to happen for far too long, I finally withdrew upstairs to my bedroom. It was inside the small room I had a eureka moment, suddenly realising I was powerless to prevent the Elliotts from telling Auntie Kathleen about my latest misdemeanour, and I also realised it was a pointless exercise fretting about things I couldn't control. I made a conscious decision to push the unease I felt to the back of my mind. Quickly the nausea that had settled in the pit of my stomach started to go away.

Feeling a little bit better, and after spending a few minutes sprawled out on the single bed, I decided it was time to get up. I quickly swapped my pyjamas for my City shirt, some shorts and a prized pair of Cheetah trainers. A kick about in the street, or in the park, was on the cards and I needed to look my best. For if there were enough of us to pick teams, it would be the first time my Hull colours had seen serious competitive action. With my mind firmly on meeting up with the local lads – including the three I got into trouble with only a day earlier, and scoring a minimum of three goals – I opened the bedroom door. And it was at that moment I became acquainted with something known in many houses as 'the piss pot'!

Unknown to me, Uncle Jim, who was carrying a chamber pot filled to the brim (for the uninitiated, it's a large bowl used to relieve the bladder before the days of the upstairs toilet and ensuite bathroom), had chosen precisely that moment to emerge from the bedroom he shared with Auntie Kathleen. They spent their nights sleeping at the front of the house. My room was situated in the centre, with Uncle Fred's to the left. The landing was tiny, dimly lit and featured a patterned brown and green wallpaper and a carpet that boasted similar colouring. The area was so small two people couldn't be in the same space together. So, when Uncle Jim and myself unwittingly decided to emerge from our rooms at the same time, there was only going to be one outcome: an utter calamity.

"Oh, you clumsy bugger," Uncle Jim exclaimed in a shocked voice as I crashed into him and the piss pot's contents sloshed everywhere. To an onlooker, it might have looked like two undernourished sumo wrestlers colliding in the most unusual of places. To us, it spelt our imminent doom. "For mercy's sake, your aunt is not going to be a happy woman, and if she's not happy, the rest of us won't be happy either," wailed Uncle Jim. "And it's all your damned fault because you didn't look where you were going."

Blowing his cheeks outward, Uncle Jim looked and sounded like he had bet his family's entire fortune on a horse that had run lame during a race, resulting in him losing everything. "Oh, my Lord. It's only all bloody well gone everywhere," he said. "It's thoroughly soaked the stairs. What the hell are we going to do now?"

He flicked on the light switch, groaning again when he saw the state of the walls, floor and his own clothing. It really wasn't a pretty sight. For my part, I was bone dry. The pot's acrid contents had missed me completely. Unaware that his hand was dripping wet, Uncle Jim ran his fingers through what was left of his dark hair and cursed yet again. Brushing his dark locks off his forehead was an act he often did when he was unsure about what to do next and panic was about to consume him.

"This is one heck of a mess, Tony," he continued. "We need to get this all sorted before your Auntie Kathleen gets wind of it. Otherwise, she really will have our guts for garters."

But our fate was already sealed. From the scullery,

Auntie Kathleen had heard the commotion and had come to investigate. By the time we realised she was within earshot, she was standing at the foot of the stairs, looking upwards with a deeply concerned expression on her face. "What has gone on, Jim?" she demanded of her husband. "You are both making one heck of a din. Is there something you need to tell me about?"

In such situations, my mum always impressed on me the need to come clean. Sadly, as his sense of panic grew, Uncle Jim did the worst thing a man can do to a woman: he tried to fob her off "Nothing's wrong, love," he said as soothingly as he could. "Tony and I were just having a little chat on the landing after he tripped on one of the stairs. It was nearly a…"

Auntie Kathleen was no mug and could see through the subterfuge instantly. She started to climb the stairs. By the time she reached the midway point, her bare feet were already soiled by the chamber pot's spilt contents.

"James Burgess," she shouted sharply. "There is something that smells remarkably like pee all over my feet. What in hell have you done, and why are you not telling me the truth?"

Uncle Jim cast a gloomy glance in my direction. His eyes carried the look of a man who was well beaten. He knew it. I knew it. And, worst of all, his silence meant Auntie Kathleen knew it.

"I think you had both better come downstairs right now and let me discover for myself what has happened. You can then answer any questions I have."

Sheepishly, Uncle Jim and I made our way down the stairs, to be met by my aunt whose face was etched with the tell-tale signs of irritation. One hand was rested on her waist, while the other was outstretched. As Uncle Jim passed her, her fingers flexed, giving the clearest indication she wanted to examine the pot.

"Bloody hell, Jim, you've spilt the lot," she said as she looked at the porcelain bowl she and my uncle had been using for decades and now rested on one of the stairs. "Everywhere is dripping in urine. Just as bad, you were trying to pull the wool over my eyes, and we'll talk about that later. In the meantime, how the heck do we get this mess tidied up before you go to work – and I have Irene Carson round for a cup of tea and some cake? She's due to be visiting me at eleven o'clock, and the house is already starting to stink like a public latrine."

Mrs Carson's name brought a smile to my face and helped me to forget about the current crisis for a moment. I hadn't seen her for several years. She was the same age as Auntie Kathleen and had married one of the Foster family cousins many moons ago. She lived on Hessle Road in Hull and was a lady who always had a smile on her face. I was quickly brought back into the present by Auntie Kathleen, who had made a decision in next to no time. "You two need to get out of here while I tidy up this mess," she said. "Jim, you've got a job to go to. So, get yourself dressed and make yourself scarce. You can get some breakfast from a cafe on your way to work. I don't need you getting under my feet when there are important things to be done, and not much time to do them."

Turning her guns on me, my aunt snapped: "And you can make yourself useful, too. Sweep needs to go out for a walk, so take him to the fields at the side of Jackson's factory, and let him do his business and have a good run around. Bring him back when he has exhausted himself. And then you'll have to look after yourself as I need to spend some time with Irene."

Auntie Kathleen was a formidable figure when she was in this kind of mood, so Uncle Jim and I did as we were told. To argue would be to potentially incur the full force of my aunt's fury, and, quite frankly, neither of us had the stomach or strength to endure that.

By the time I returned from my walk with Sweep, who displayed the energy and vitality of a giant sloth rather than a canine hunter, Uncle Jim was long gone and Auntie Kathleen had done as much as she could to make good the sodden stairs.

"That's all I am going to be able to do in the time I have at my disposal," she said, rising to her feet, her cheeks flushed from the effort of cleaning. "Thanks to you and your clumsy uncle, there will be work to be done tonight when he gets back from work. But it'll do. Now, have you got anything you can be getting on with for the next few hours, while I spend some time with Irene? We have a lot to talk about and catch up on…"

"As luck would have it, there is something I can do," I said. "If you don't mind, I'll go for a walk and take my football with me, just in case I get the chance to have a kick about. Is that okay?"

Auntie Kathleen had too much on her mind to object. I could have said anything and she would happily have agreed to it. The fact I had just been out walking her dog didn't matter one bit. If she hadn't been distracted with other things, I am sure she would have grilled me a bit more thoroughly. Thankfully she didn't, which meant I could repay the debt owed to Mr and Mrs Elliott. So, I got myself ready to eat humble pie and do some hard labour.

By the time it got close to five o'clock, all thoughts of the piss pot debacle had long been forgotten, and cordial and loving relations between Auntie Kathleen and Uncle Jim were well and truly restored. I had visited the Elliotts at midday and done my penance, much to the delight of the forgiving newsagents. It had only taken thirty minutes, or so, to load the lorry, which meant I had ample time to find a park and kick my ball about. And they even gave me a fizzy drink as a reward for a "job well done". The irony didn't escape me. By the time I returned to number thirteen, I was worn out. It's one thing kicking a ball about for fun, quite something else when you have to lift crate after heavy crate onto the back of a lorry. Sweep was in a similar state to me, having experienced the same kind of exhausted reaction to his morning walk and had remained motionless for the duration of Irene's visit, which – by the look on Auntie Kathleen's face – had been a very happy occasion. With my aunt in a good mood, laughter and merriment were soon echoing off the inner walls of number thirteen once again.

Alas, work still needed to be completed on the stairs and landing, as Auntie Kathleen had only been able to tackle half of the clean-up operation, such had been the extent of the spillage. No sooner had our forks finished off the delicious shepherd's pie that had been made for us, than Uncle Jim and myself were ordered back to the stairs so we could start scrubbing the carpet and eliminating the awful stink of the *you know what!*

"Well, we bloody well pulled the short straw on this one, didn't we?" muttered my rueful uncle as he rolled up his shirt sleeves and got stuck into the unedifying task. "I've been telling your aunt we needed to get a bigger pot for months. But she ignored me. And lo and behold, this happens. Typical! Now, why don't you take yourself to your bedroom, and do something more enjoyable and productive than this, and I'll crack on and get it all sorted. Your aunt will be none the wiser."

In truth, he wanted me out of the way because I would slow down the cleaning process. On his own, the job would take twenty minutes. With me alongside him, you were looking at double the amount of time because Uncle Jim would be required to check everything I did and make up for any inadequacies he found, and there would undoubtedly be plenty. Hard graft was not one of my strong points. So, as I went to my bedroom to play once again with my toy soldiers, Uncle Jim cracked on and set about making good, which he did without breaking sweat. Once in my room, I could clearly hear him whistling and talking to himself. I got the feeling he was enjoying the peace and quiet of being on his own for a moment, even if it had come at a cost.

By the time tea was ready, Uncle Jim had changed into a clean pair of trousers and a freshly laundered shirt and found time to come downstairs, sit himself down in the front room and start snoozing in his chair. It didn't take long for his presence to be discovered as he started snoring almost immediately – very loudly. I had already sat down at the table in the scullery when Auntie Kathleen called out again. "Wake up, Jim. Your tea is getting cold." Despite the prompting, there was no movement from her dozing spouse. So she shouted once more, and then a third time, this time with a sliver of irritation becoming apparent in her voice. Alas, Uncle Jim just sat there, dead to the world. It was at that moment I saw the wicked glint in Auntie Kathleen's eye. As I looked on, I saw her reach inside the kitchen cupboard and take out a small gong – a bit like the one used at the start of all Metro Goldwyn Mayer movies. Moving quietly, she tip-toed towards Uncle Jim, who remained asleep and totally at her mercy. His head was lifted to the ceiling and his arms hung limply on either side of the chair. With a devilish grin, she stopped and looked momentarily at me, before laughing and striking the gong with the precision of a seasoned percussionist. The small instrument was positioned just an inch, or two, away from Uncle Jim's right ear, and the sound shattered the peace of the house. Sweep woke up instantly and howled as if someone had stamped on his tail, while my poor, traumatised uncle leapt out of his chair, his arms flailing. "What-what-what in God's name is going on?" he spluttered. "What the heck is happening?"

At the sight of her befuddled husband jumping up and down like a bouncing ball, Auntie Kathleen dissolved into fits of laughter. I, too, couldn't contain myself. "You leave yourself wide open every week, Jim," she said, her voice laced with affection. "You have been warned so many times that if you fall asleep at teatime, you must face the consequences. And yet you do the same thing time and time again. You make it so easy for me."

"I am glad my misfortune has made you two so happy," said the crestfallen victim, once his heart had resumed a normal beat and his blood pressure had regularised itself. "That prank of yours will kill me one day either through a heart attack, or a stroke. You mark my words, I will be a goner by the time I am sixty if you carry on doing things like that. For goodness sake, I can't believe a grown-up woman would set such an example to a young lad. What's Tony going to think? He'll be justified in telling himself it's quite alright to play more tricks on poor old Uncle Jim. Why? Because his Auntie Kathleen does just that."

The outburst provoked more chuckles from my aunt. I laughed, too. And even Uncle Jim eventually started to see the funny side of things after a short while. "Okay, you win," he conceded, raising both hands. "You got me good and proper this time round. But please, can you widen your scope of attack in the future. Can't you pick on Fred a bit more than you do and give me a bit of a rest? Being the butt of your pranks and jokes is getting a bit tiresome."

Mention of Uncle Fred's name changed the mood completely. He was a man who was plagued by a series of accidental misfortunes, which usually meant he always escaped when pranks were being played. The view of most members of the family was that Uncle Fred was a bit 'simple'. It was a view my mum had held for the last few years, formed after an incident that occurred in 1971 when he did his utmost to accidentally kill himself.

For as long as anyone could remember, Uncle Fred had loved the thrill of bikes – the pedal and motorised versions. During the daytime, he could be found on his Raleigh bike racing across country lanes to RAF Leconfield, where he worked as a labourer. On Sundays, he jumped into the saddle and travelled a few, short miles to the River Humber, where he spent the whole day watching the construction of the mighty bridge linking East Yorkshire to Lincolnshire. This he did for eight years. At other times, he retired to the wooden shed in the back garden. This is where he once kept his trusty moped, a contraption that looked and sounded as though it had seen its best days at the turn of the century.

Like all members of the Burgess side of the family, Uncle Fred was a smoker, and he would often light up when he was hard at work in the shed. One evening, he decided it was a good idea to mix two-stroke petrol with paraffin. Fred wasn't happy with the options available at the local run-of-the-mill garages, he wanted something with a bit more oomph – which meant he had to innovate. It was as he was seeking to create a super fuel that would power his 50cc contraption through the streets of Cottingham and beyond, that disaster struck: his lit cigarette fell from his mouth and into an open bucket of fuel he was stirring. Instantly, it ignited and Uncle Fred, in a desperate attempt to extinguish the fire with his hands, was engulfed in flames. By the time he crashed out of the shed, most of his lower body was burning. Auntie Kathleen witnessed the inferno and thinking quickly, she was able to rush out and smother him in a blanket, an act that almost certainly saved him from serious injury, or worse. But she could do nothing to prevent the moped's petrol tank from exploding and the entire shed from being destroyed. The episode ensured the *Hull Daily Mail* printed a couple of prominent stories about Uncle Fred's close shave with death, and gained him near legendary status with the whole family, as well as affording him an element of protection as far as taking the Mickey out of him was concerned.

"Okay you two, tuck in," said Auntie Kathleen in an encouraging voice when all thoughts had returned to food.

"Let's enjoy our tea, stop pulling Uncle Jim's leg, and get ourselves ready to have some fun this evening."

Without any further encouragement, we duly obliged.

I felt tired and utterly contented by the time Reginald Bosanquet's ruddy features appeared on the box that evening. Auntie Kathleen and Uncle Jim preferred to watch *News at Ten* on ITV, rather than the BBC's offering an hour earlier, and Bosanquet was their favourite news-reader. We had just enjoyed a fruitful couple of hours play-ing cards, one of our favourite pastimes. And after starting off with a few hands of Rummy, we progressed to Newmarket – which I excelled at, winning three of the five contests – before closing proceedings with Fives, a combat-ive game that pitted everyone against one another, and brought the best, and worst, of our personalities out into the open. It was Auntie Jessie's favourite game, but in her absence, Auntie Kathleen, or myself, usually claimed top dog status.

"I don't know why I bother!" exclaimed Uncle Jim on more than one occasion as he was routed time and again. "I have got no chance when you two get your eye in."

That particular evening, after we had tired of playing cards, we settled down to watch the news. If I am honest, it was a programme that bored me to death, going on, as it usually did, about Margaret Thatcher and a couple of blokes called Jim Callaghan and Denis Healey, the useless British car industry (particularly the problems at British Leyland), not to forget the downturn in fortunes of the England football team. Although I was generally disinterested in the events of the world, I knew when times were good, and when they were not. And right now, it appeared Great Britain was in a bit of a mess.

I had just started to take a keen interest in the news when a shocked and sombre-looking Reginald Bosanquet announced: "Elvis Presley, the king of rock and roll, is dead." It was almost ten thirty. Auntie Kathleen and Uncle Jim immediately fell silent. I followed suit. We watched as more details of the demise of the forty-two-year-old were relayed to a stunned TV audience, and it felt like a bomb had been detonated in this little bit of East Yorkshire. We sat there, listening and taking it all in, not quite believing what we were being told. Could Elvis really be dead? The minutes ticked away. And then Auntie Kathleen started to sniffle and dab the corners of her eyes. "What a terrible shame," she said as Reginald Bosanquet's image faded from the telly screen and the end credits started to roll. "He's going to be missed by so many people, including by Ann." Mention of my mum's name immediately put me on a state of high alert. Knowing how much she loved Elvis, I knew how upset she would be by his death. But it seemed not everyone held such feelings.

"For goodness sake, he was just a singer who got lucky," said Uncle Jim, scratching his head, unable to understand why his wife was emotional about a man she had never met and whose music meant nothing to them. "Admittedly, he had a bit of talent, but he was nothing special. If anything, he was damned lucky to have the kind of success he had. I really can't see what all the fuss is about, and I really don't know why you are blubbing?"

They were not the kindest of words. And Uncle Jim instantly regretted expressing such forthright views.

"James Burgess, on occasion you can be a cold-hearted so-and-so and a very unlikeable man," said Auntie Kathleen, not hiding her displeasure. "I suggest you take the dog out for a nighttime walk. Take as long as you need. But, when you come back, make sure you don't repeat sentiments like the ones you have just expressed. A normal person should feel very sad at hearing such news. So, don't come home until you do or, at the very least, you can keep a lid on your unpleasant views."

Auntie Kathleen's words struck home and within a couple of minutes, Uncle Jim had fled the scene, dragging the reluctant Sweep with him. As the gate to the backyard closed, and the sound of Uncle Jim's footsteps started to fade, the house phone started to ring. By then, it was close to eleven o'clock, way past my bedtime. Even so, the piercing ringtone could not be ignored. But before Auntie Kathleen took the call, she looked up at me and blew me a kiss.

"Now, off to bed with you," she urged. "Sleep well. I am looking forward to whipping you again at cards."

We both chuckled at the prospect. Then, doing as I had been instructed, I climbed the sweet-smelling stairs. As I reached the top, Auntie Kathleen picked up the phone. "Hello, love," I heard her say. "I thought you would call, even at this late hour about this terrible news. It's so unexpected. He was always your favourite. Do you remember when…"

It was my mum calling. I would learn some years later that she stayed on the phone for almost two hours, being gently consoled by Auntie Kathleen, who always knew what to say, and was always willing to invest as much time as was needed in the people she cared about most. ✳

FOUR

Lies. Damned lies. And tanks

WITH THE STORY ABOUT ELVIS'S death dominating the television, radio, and daily newspaper headlines, we were desperate for some respite to lift the state of doom and gloom that had taken a hold of all our lives. It duly came on Thursday, the eighteenth day of August, when Auntie Maureen and Uncle Archie returned to their home at number sixteen Brockenhurst Avenue. It was located directly opposite Auntie Kathleen and Uncle Jim's abode. Coincidentally, it was the day 'The King' was buried thousands of miles away in Memphis.

Maureen was my mum's youngest sister. Just like her, she had bright, auburn hair that meant it was impossible to remain anonymous in a crowd. She had many great qualities, including a wonderful sense of humour and a caring heart. But she didn't suffer fools gladly, so you always had to be careful about what you said (although I was lucky enough to never incur her wrath). I loved my aunt dearly. She had, after all, helped to raise me when she was only seventeen years old. I was newly born, mum had to work every day at Northern Dairies in Hull, and Auntie Maureen was called upon to play nursemaid for much of the working week. This created a special bond between us, which meant I always enjoyed her company, much of which was spent laughing and talking about family members and bygone times. Within a couple of years of my birth, she followed in the footsteps of her siblings and left home to join the Royal Navy, where she met and fell in love with my Uncle Archie. Together, they spent the first few years of marriage building a happy life – adopting along the way a delightful mongrel called Mac. As he closed in on his forty-seventh birthday, Uncle Archie's retirement from the navy was confirmed and they decided to leave Tayside, where they had lived for several years while he served on the Ark Royal aircraft carrier, opting to move to Cottingham, of which she noted: "The place looks exactly as it did when I left." From her new home, Maureen quickly settled back into village life, while Archie began a new chapter in civvy street after many years of service defending Queen and country. To cap things off, just a few weeks earlier they had welcomed their first child into the world. Emma, my cousin, had been born on the twentieth day of June.

While delighted I would be able to spend time with them all and meet my cousin for the first time (although I was clueless about what you did with a baby), I had no idea they would be returning home. I was led to believe I wouldn't see them at all during my stay. They had gone to Kirkaldy in Scotland (or Kuh-kaw-dee, as the Scots prefer to pronounce it) to visit Uncle Archie's mother, but something unknown to my Auntie Kathleen and Uncle Jim had necessitated an early return. And while I was very eager to be reacquainted with them, a sense of unease gnawed away at me, born less than twelve months earlier when I did a 'swap' with the son of one of Uncle Archie's old naval friends. They had been visiting Yorkshire when I was on last year's two-week pilgrimage, and their boy, called Jeremy, had some toys I desperately wanted. I traded an assortment of small soldiers and the like, but I also promised I would give him one of my coveted Airfix Churchill tanks, via Uncle Archie, who would ensure its safe passage to the lands north of Hadrian's Wall. The deal meant I immediately got my hands on some Action Man clobber I desperately wanted, while Jeremy graciously (and very trustingly) agreed to wait to receive the tank. Unfortunately, I hadn't yet fulfilled my side of the bargain, and I now feared my day of reckoning had arrived.

"Anyone would think there was a bad smell in the room," exclaimed Auntie Kathleen when my face remained neutral after she had passed on the good news about Auntie Maureen and Uncle Archie's homecoming. "I thought you would be pleased to see your aunt and uncle, after all, you are always talking about them. And then there's Mac, who will need a lot of walking after the long journey from Scotland. Surely that, at least, is a reason to be jolly?"

Thankfully, Auntie Kathleen was unaware of the truth. If she knew what I had done, I fear she would have had a few choice words to say herself. As it was, I only had to worry about meeting Auntie Maureen and Uncle Archie and using the time I had left to come up with a plausible excuse for my behaviour. Under normal circumstances, I was usually up to this kind of task, having gained a reputation for pulling the wool over people's eyes. What concerned me more than anything was, even if I came up with the perfect reason for not handing over the tank, Uncle Archie had this uncanny knack of cutting through what he referred to in his Scottish accent as "utter bull shite", and I feared his withering gaze and interrogation would leave me totally exposed. Therefore, in a bid to settle down and hatch a cunning plan, I asked Auntie Kathleen if I could take Sweep for a walk. Mercifully, it was a request she always agreed to, so I took the dog's lead from its peg and fastened it securely to the mutt's collar. As I did so, he looked at me with utter contempt. We both knew I was disturbing his walk-rest cycle, for he never went out in the morning. Without making a noise, he made it perfectly clear he was comfortable and wanted to stay put. To emphasise the point, he stretched out on his blanket under the table and extended his rear and front legs while emitting the guttural sounds of a thoroughly contented animal. I realised I would have to be at my most persuasive to get him to comply with my wishes. But within a few seconds of trying to cajole him out of his pit, I was engaged in a battle of wills, and this was a fight I daren't lose. So, with nobody looking in the general direction of the front room, I used my right foot to apply some pressure to one of Sweep's paws, which caught him completely by surprise. He yelped, turned onto his stomach and, in a single movement, got up, expelling one of those foul, dog breath smells from his mouth as he attempted to shake off his acute drowsiness and the sudden pain I had inflicted. That's the moment I had him. A quick yank on the dog lead enabled me to regain my dominance, and with supremacy safely re-established, we were out of the door before you could shout "Scooby Do".

The walk lasted longer than I expected, a full two hours no less. Surprisingly, Sweep was as good as gold, only disgracing himself on one occasion when he attempted to impregnate an innocent-looking King Charles Spaniel whose inquisitiveness was nearly its undoing, much to the horror of its owner. Thankfully, I was able to drag my ungainly ball of fur off the unsuspecting victim before any lasting damage was done, and after mumbling several profound apologies and promising to be a more responsible owner, the walk continued down Thwaite Street, across the railway crossing and into the centre of Cottingham. It was a lovely day, one that should have seen me kicking my football on the field down the Lane, preparing for City's big match against Sunderland, and not fretting about things. Thankfully, I was outdoors, the fresh air was doing some good and, without realising it, I was heading towards food – my constant source of comfort. On this occasion, I was making my way to Skeltons, a popular bakery that produced Yorkshire curd cheesecakes, one of the greatest concoctions to have ever blessed the oven.

Before I had reached the shop I knew so well, I had fumbled in my pockets and found a fifty pence piece. By my reckoning, that would buy me at least two curd cakes and may secure me a drink of orange juice as well. And so it proved to be, with the lady who served me adding a third cake in my bag that she said wasn't fit to sell. I ate these Yorkshire delicacies in rapid succession as we walked past Saint Mary's Church, which mum and I once attended, and the primary school, where I used to go until we moved to Leicestershire. Then I found the narrow snicket that ran past the walled playground. It would take us back all the way to Hull Road, and ultimately home.

When I was first introduced to the curd cheesecake by aunts Kathleen and Jessie, I was amazed at how something that was quite underwhelming in appearance could taste so good. And every time I have subsequently bought this treat, I have continued to experience these very same feelings. Thankfully, regardless of their lack of cosmetic appeal, the cakes helped to change my mood. For much of the return part of the walk, I told myself it might just be my lucky day if I could only find a good excuse to placate my aunt and uncle! But however I dressed things up and attempted to justify my behaviour of the last twelve months, there was no escaping the realisation: I was in the wrong, it was as simple as that! The stark reality was my only path to redemption was to take whatever punishment was bestowed on me – and give the tank to Uncle Archie, so he could belatedly give it to Jeremy. If my mum had become aware of things, I suspect she would have barred me from going to Saturday's match, grounding me at least for the weekend. So, as we got closer to the rooftops of the Avenue, I prayed my Auntie Maureen and Uncle Archie would be in a merciful mood.

"Well, look who it is. Our very own Fagan has returned to the robber's den," boomed Uncle Archie, as I walked into the scullery, carrying the authority of a man who once held rank in the navy. "What ill-gotten gains have you brought with you today?"

Much to my alarm and disappointment, Auntie Maureen and Uncle Archie had enjoyed a good journey home, arriving back in Cottingham almost an hour earlier than expected. By the time Sweep and I made it back to number thirteen, they had unpacked their suitcases, tidied things up and made their way to Auntie Kathleen's for a cup of tea and a catch-up. And to wait for me. Auntie Kathleen and Auntie Maureen laughed heartily at the quip, thinking Uncle Archie was pulling my leg, as he often did in a good-natured way. But I knew the truth, as did he.

"So what have you got to tell us?" enquired Auntie Maureen seemingly unaware of my betrayal twelve months earlier. She was perched on the settee holding what I presumed was Emma, my baby cousin, who seemed to be fast asleep. "How's home? How's your mum?" Auntie Maureen was always interested in how we were doing. So, I told her, warts and all. She learned mum was still adjusting to a new kind of life after the divorce from my step-father, and she heard about Leicestershire, and how we both continued to struggle to settle into our new home. After a while, she sighed heavily; Auntie Maureen had heard enough.

"It sounds like this break has come at just the right time for you," she said, unable to mask her concern. "I am really glad Uncle Archie came home early. How about we do something nice over the next few days. Does that sound like a good idea?"

I didn't need to utter a word to indicate I was in complete agreement. My body language conveyed more than any book could ever do.

"Good," continued Auntie Maureen. "Is there anything you fancy doing? The seaside, maybe, or perhaps we can go on a trip somewhere, after all there's loads to do and see in God's county?"

I would have been happy doing anything if it meant going out with my aunts and uncle and having a good time. But Uncle Archie had an idea to beat all others.

"How about we go on a picnic to the North Yorkshire Moors?" he suggested. "We can take sandwiches, cake and pop with us, maybe play some games and the like while we're up there, and then have a Chinese on the way home. Does that meet with the approval of everyone?"

The suggestion was greeted enthusiastically by all. Even Sweep, who certainly wouldn't be allowed to come along, thumped his tail on the floor in approval. I had only been to the Moors once before, but I remember it being a huge open expanse of land, comprising more than five hundred square miles stretching as far as the eyes could see. It took in towns and places like Helmsley, Whitby, Guisborough and Ravenscar. 'Beautiful' wasn't a word I used very often, it was a bit too effusive for my liking. Yet it is very apt when describing this enchanting part of Yorkshire. After discussing possible places of interest, it was decided we'd head towards the spa town of Harrogate, a journey of about an hour and three-quarters. Five of us would be going – Uncle Archie, aunts Kathleen, Maureen and Jessie, as well as myself – and although it would be a squeeze, we'd somehow find a way of getting us all in the car even if it meant stowing me in the boot. Our day for adventure was set for tomorrow, the nine-teenth day of August – the day before Auntie Maureen's birthday (another family event I was looking forward to). We'd be leaving by ten o'clock in the morning, on pain of death, and Emma would be staying behind in Cottingham with a neighbour and good friend of Auntie Maureen's who just had her own second child and insisted on doing some babysitting (as a tot, Emma spent about twenty hours a day sleeping, so there were unlikely to be any complica-tions). Our goal was to get to our destination by lunchtime, without the need for Uncle Archie to set any land speed records in his Ford Cortina. It also meant I'd get the chance to sample my first-ever Chinese meal, as Auntie Maureen had requested we return specifically via Beverley, where she knew of a sit-down restaurant that made the very best Chow Mein. I wasn't sure what that was, but I was definitely keen on trying it, particularly as the meal would be an early treat for my aunt, whose birthday it was the following day.

As we all contemplated the hastily arranged trip, Uncle Archie stood up, looked directly at me and said: "Tony, come and help me make a cup of tea, and pick up your aunts' cups and bring them through." Immediately, my stomach spasmed and a sense of dread took hold.

Auntie Kathleen remarked: "Are you okay?. You are as white as a sheet and look as though you have just seen a ghost." I shrugged my shoulders and flashed a forced smile, inside, however, I was all churned up. I suspected my uncle was choosing this very moment to hold me to account. And these fears intensified as I walked into the scullery where he had already started washing the dishes.

"Just pop those cups and saucers down there," he said when he was sure the ladies were all having a conversation about what tomorrow would bring. "And grab a tea towel. I will wash and you can do the drying."

We set about the task, neither of us offering up another word. For a handful of minutes, the silence became all-consuming. When I got to drying the last cup, Uncle Archie broke the spell. "You and I need to resolve something Tony, and I am sure you know what I am talking about?" he said firmly, without any trace of anger in his voice. "Of course you do. You know very well what you did last year was wrong, and so do I. Only you know why you did it, but we'll talk about it again sometime later, and we will also agree on how you will put right the wrong you committed. For now, let's agree that this matter remains between you and me. Auntie Maureen knows nothing about it. Neither does your mum. And they won't, just as long as you can convince me you will do the right thing as far as that blessed tank is concerned."

With that, Uncle Archie returned to the sitting room, leaving me to make the tea and digest what had just been said. It was clear I wasn't out of jail by any stretch. But neither was I being hanged, drawn and quartered. And I didn't need to tell a fib, or make a ridiculous excuse; my uncle had spared me that. The tension in my stomach began to ease and by the time I took the tea through to my parched aunts, the colour had returned to my cheeks. I had been granted a reprieve, and all I needed to do was make sure I didn't mess up again. I closed my eyes, recalled the prayers I had been taught at Sunday School, and spoke quietly with my Maker. "Thank you," I said, my hands clasped tightly together as my gaze adopted an upward trajectory. "Thank you." ✳

FIVE

Getting a buzz on the Yorkshire moors

WITH UNCLE ARCHIE MARSHALLING proceedings in his own house and number thirteen with military precision, we had no difficulty in meeting the agreed ten o'clock departure time on Friday morning.

Auntie Jessie, who was always the most likely candidate to cause a delay, as she had to travel to Cottingham on the bus, had risen early and was knocking on the front door a good hour before we were due to leave. By then, Auntie Kathleen was dressed, washed, and able to beckon her sister inside with the lure of a fresh cup of tea, a slice of toast and the finest Seville orange marmalade (coarsely cut, of course). Meanwhile, in the house opposite, Auntie Maureen and Uncle Archie had been making trips to the boot of their Ford Cortina, packing away enough food to feed an entire city, not just the five of us. While there was undoubtedly a lot of effort being expended by the adults, the same couldn't be said about me. I was loafing around in my pyjamas and was neither washed nor breakfasted. Auntie Kathleen had looked directly at me several times but hadn't said anything. So, when she did, I was rather surprised by the volume of her voice and her clipped tone.

"Will you stop dawdling and go and get yourself dressed," she snapped as she caught me watching Auntie Maureen and Uncle Archie have a minor squabble about which side of the boot some of the food should be packed. "And be quick about it. I have got some jobs I need you to do before we set off. So, no sitting in your bedroom and day dreaming. Let's be having you."

As I made myself scarce and started climbing the stairs (where remnants of the strong disinfectant used to clean up after the other day's disaster still lingered in the air), I heard my two aunts start chatting about their hopes and aspirations for the trip. "It's lovely to be getting out," said Auntie Kathleen. "I can't remember the last time I went to Harrogate. It must be at least twenty years. So, I am going to make up for some lost time by having a large slice of cake at Betty's."

Auntie Jessie was equally enthusiastic about visiting one of Yorkshire's most famous tea shops: "Me, too," she responded. "We've been cooped up for far too long, so Betty's is a long overdue treat. And we'll also have a nice meal in Beverley to look forward to, although I don't think I have ever had Chinese food before, so that'll be a first. I hope I like it. I am a bit suspicious of all this foreign stuff."

Even though I had just been chastised, hearing my aunts talk so affectionately to one another, and hearing the sense of anticipation in their voices, fired up my own enthusiasm for the venture, which didn't include Uncle Jim, as he was out today plying his trade in Orchard Park; my apprehension about spending time with Auntie Maureen and Uncle Archie had been forgotten after yesterday's man-to-man conversation. I quickly dressed with the minimum of fuss. My underpants had been worn for only three days, so they were still 'clean', and my socks did-n't yet have that ripe smell that indicates they needed washing, so I quickly pulled them on too. Unfortunately, I had to pass on the chance to wear City's colours, having been ordered to don a clean, plain t-shirt instead. The decisive factor was the sweat-infused odour coming from the armpits of my Hull top, and Auntie Kathleen's edict that I must wear something a 'bit smarter and cleaner'. I wasn't too unhappy. Best to leave the football shirt to air for a day, so it would be fine for tomorrow's big match.

I returned to the sitting room, wearing, to all intents and purposes, freshly laundered clothing, much to the delight of both my aunts. "Oh, that's so much better, Tony," said Auntie Jessie, as she sipped up the final last drops of tea from her cup. "You look very smart. Now, all you have to do is make sure you keep yourself clean all day. Do you think that's possible?"

We all laughed at that comment for, with the exception of my Tigers shirt, I was known to be a child who attracted filth and could get as black as the ace of spades while having a bath. When the chuckling had run its course, Auntie Kathleen returned to the subject of the jobs she wanted me to do before our departure. "Now young man," she said, looking at me from the comfort of her front room throne. "There is some laundry that needs hanging out on the washing line. You will find it next to the mangle. Do your best to get it all hanging in neat rows, so the wind can do its business while we're out. I'll give you ten minutes, or so, to get it sorted. Now, off with you and get the job done."

And so, mindful I needed to earn some 'good lad points', I did as my aunt asked, while eagerly awaiting the call that would indicate it was time to be on our way.

By midday, we had reached the outskirts of Harrogate. But instead of heading directly towards the historic spa town, we continued along the A61, until we reached the Skipton Road, a vital thoroughfare that headed directly towards Menwith Hill. This, I had learned on the journey, was home to the famous RAF radar station that served as an early warning system should the Soviet Union ever decide to unleash its nuclear arsenal at Britain and NATO. The base was notable because it had a series of white outbuildings, which resembled a pair of giant golf balls. Inside, top-secret military technologies were reputedly housed .

Uncle Archie had changed our destination at the last minute – when we were well underway – and it certainly wasn't a popular move with the female majority in the car. "Why aren't we going to Harrogate?" remonstrated Auntie Maureen. Although she had left Emma in the charge of a good friend and a highly experienced mum, the stress of leaving her daughter was starting to show. "We were looking forward to a nice cup of tea and a stroll around the town. Now, all we'll see are rooftops in the far-off distance, and have to sit on the grass, which will set off Auntie Jessie good and proper. You know her bum goes numb if she hasn't got cushions to sit on."

On cue, Auntie Jessie started to make some noises which confirmed her own lack of approval. Yet despite the mounting protests, Uncle Archie remained undeterred. "You will all love it when we are up there," he reassured them. "The views are stunning and where we're going will be nice and quiet. I doubt whether we'll see another living soul. And there is the added bonus of it being the perfect place to fly a kite, and you're up for a bit of that, aren't you Tony?"

Mention of my name brought me out of the trance-like state I often found myself entering on car journeys when adults talked about things I had no interest in. But the mention of kite flying brought me back to life instantly. "I certainly am," I agreed enthusiastically.

The revelation we had a kite in the car was news to me. Judging by Auntie Maureen's expression, it was also news to her. My uncle had not said a word about it yesterday, therefore the surprise was complete, one that immediately raised my spirits. The announcement also meant I strongly supported the decision, something I am sure Uncle Archie had factored into his thinking when he smuggled it into the car. "You are going to love it, Tony," he continued. "I have got the perfect kite for the occasion. It looks just like the one I had when I was your age, only better. And I have bought some extra balls of string that we can attach to it, which means we'll be able to fly it even higher than normal – and do some stunts. We can take turns flying it and let your aunts have a good chat while we're having a lot of fun."

I was hooked, albeit I wasn't convinced the kite had made the journey just for my benefit.

My excitement mounted as the car climbed up the winding road to our eventual destination, a lay-by conveniently located on the brow of one of the rolling hills that dominated as far as the naked eye could see. Not so far away, protected by the barbed wires of RAF Menwith, were the enormous white orbs that housed the powerful and essential radars. If I were to guess the distance, I would say they were only a mile, or so, away from where the Cortina was parked.

The next forty-five minutes passed slowly. Ordinarily, I would have taken as much time as possible eating the various stockpiles of sandwiches, cake, and crisps, and drinking several glasses of pop. But not today. The idea of kite flying had captured my imagination, and I couldn't wait to complete my maiden flight. Eventually, after he had sipped his second cuppa at the pace of a snail, and the mood of my aunts had thawed, Uncle Archie was ready for action. "Okay, let's crack on," he said to me. "It's time to get to work."

Reaching into one of the bags we had retrieved from the car, he pulled out four large balls of string, each measuring approximately a hundred feet in length. Next to emerge was the kite itself, still in its packaging. Once unwrapped, it looked so small, yet when fully extended it was a good three feet in length and just over a couple of feet wide. At its centre was a black skull and crossbones emblem, and it had a tail that must have measured at least twenty feet in length. When airborne, it certainly wouldn't go unnoticed. Two controls, one for either hand, would enable us to weave the structure across the skies, pulling stunts at will. Uncle Archie looked as eager as I was to get things underway. So, we walked a hundred, or so, yards away from the car and women folk and set about our task. As always, safety, rather than speed, was of the essence.

"Let's get the string attached, making sure the knots are tight and secure," pleaded Uncle Archie who, being a navy man, knew a thing, or two, about tying ropes together. "We don't want to get everything sorted only for the bloody strings to come loose. That would be a disaster your Auntie Maureen would never let me forget."

Within a few minutes, we had achieved our goal: the kite had been successfully constructed and tested by Uncle Archie, who ensured everything was fit for purpose. Needing little prompting, I took hold of it, and then, working to my uncle's instruction, positioned myself in the best possible place to ensure the maximum lift to get it airborne. Alas, when I stopped, I found myself standing in the middle of a large smattering of heather that concealed one of the greatest known dangers to children – a fresh cowpat, newly deposited by one of the many cattle that roamed the moors. To make matters worse, my right foot was completely submerged in its wet centre.

After he became aware of my misfortune, Uncle Archie howled with laughter. "Just make sure you don't move an inch," he said. "And when the kite is flying, watch carefully where you're treading. Your aunts have a very keen sense of smell, so there is no way you'll be wearing your trainers in the car now you've trodden in one."

That was as much sympathy as I got because our attention quickly returned to the job at hand. Thankfully, I didn't have long to think about my own predicament as Uncle Archie pulled tight on the cords, which was my signal to release the kite. I did, and as if by a miracle, it gained height rapidly. Uncle Archie's hands were working furiously to unravel the string cords, as the wind tugged on the kite, urging it further upwards. As more and more of the cord was released, it continued to rise, until the reel was spent. "That's as far as it will go," shouted Uncle Archie, his excitement as great as my own. "It must be flying at well over two hundred and fifty feet."

As he spoke, Uncle Archie pulled down on one cord, and then applied pressure to the other. As if by magic, the kite weaved in the sky doing a manoeuvre known as the 'Figure of Eight'. Its long tail tried to keep up with the main body, but it was always slightly out of sync. The result was a fabulous sight, one that drew appreciative comments and gasps from my three aunts, who briefly suspended their conversation to watch a kite-flying masterclass. With their voices quietened, all that could be heard was the wind racing over the moorland and the engines of the occasional car and lorry that passed by. As my focus remained firmly fixed on the kite, I started to walk forward. Instantly I realised it was a mistake I was powerless to correct. The sole of my left foot had barely touched the ground when I realised it had found another cowpat. Horrified, I looked down to see it was totally submerged. My Cheetah trainers were caked in cow muck. But before I had time to think about the magnitude of my mistake, Uncle Archie barked out excitedly. "Jets," he yelled. "By the look of them, they're a pair of Lightnings."

I looked up, just as the boom of the engines of the two sleek fighter planes erupted over our heads. Grey, and with their distinctive shape illuminating the sky, the aircraft were flying at a low altitude and were very close to our own position. We watched them as they carried out a circling manoeuvre around the area where we were standing, travelling at a speed that was hard to comprehend. They seemed to be taking an interest in the hill where we were.

"What are they doing?" I asked my uncle, all thoughts of my cowpat-encrusted feet forgotten. "They just seem to be flying in a big circle." And so they were. Once. Twice. Three times the planes buzzed around the hill, like wasps checking out a jam jar that's been left open on the kitchen table at the height of summer. And every time, they seemed to get lower, so we could clearly see their numbering, insignia and the outlines of the pilots in their cockpits.

"Bloody hell! They're checking us out," roared Uncle Archie suddenly. "The kite must have registered on the radars, and they have scrambled a couple of planes to see what is going on. We've got to get out of here, or we're going to find ourselves in a lot of trouble."

As his words trailed off, Uncle Archie let go of the kite's dual controls. With nobody steering its path, it veered across the sky, spiralling one way, and then another, its haphazard journey all the more visible due to the length of its tail. For a moment, it looked as though it was thriving on its newfound freedom. Then it was held up in the wind, before crashing to the ground seventy yards away. Ironically, it met its doom in a large cowpat.

"Let's get going, Tony," shouted Uncle Archie, as I continued to look in the direction of the downed kite, as the jets roared over one more time before heading off in the direction from where they had come. There was no disguising the urgency in his voice. Turning his attention to my aunts, who had bewildered looks on their faces and clearly didn't understand why their peace had suddenly been shattered, Uncle Archie was equally economical with his choice of words. "Whatever are you looking at, ladies?" he called. "Get into the car before we all find ourselves in real trouble. We need to get going as quickly as possible."

Never have my aunts Kathleen, Jessie and Maureen moved so quickly. Unceremoniously, what was left of our picnic was thrown into any available bag, and any tea sloshing in a cup, or pot, was emptied onto the wild grass and bracken. Blankets were lifted up and taken back to the car and thrown in the boot without being folded – which only ever happened in the gravest of emergencies. With the jet engines fading, but still audible, we beat a hasty retreat. For at least five minutes nobody spoke. We were all in a state of shock. The only person who seemed to be in control of his senses was Uncle Archie, whose wheel spin out of the lay-by and onto the Skipton Road was straight out of the books of *The Sweeney*, the midweek TV detective series many millions of people watched every week.

After she had regained her composure, Auntie Maureen was the first to start the inquisition. "What the hell was all that about, Archie?" she demanded. "Why have we got the RAF breathing down our necks?" Her questions were the trigger for my other aunts to join in, and very quickly the car became filled with noise, as one voice became mingled with another. The cacophony continued for at least four miles until Uncle Archie spotted a lay-by. Decreasing his speed, he pulled in, just ahead of a Scammell lorry carrying a wagon load of sheep. He quickly turned off the engine. It was only after he had checked his rear and side mirrors did he dare to breathe a sigh of relief – but his respite only lasted a few seconds.

"You pillock, what have you just gone and done?" rang out the alarmed voice of Auntie Maureen. Her face was flushed and set. She was speaking up for herself and aunts Kathleen and Jessie, who were still confused by everything that had happened. Turning around to face his accusers, Uncle Archie said: "I think we may have triggered the early warning system at Menwith Hill. With hindsight, perhaps it wasn't a good idea to increase the length of the kite's strings, like we did. There must be a maximum height you are allowed to fly these things. Anything above that must trigger the system, which then results in jets being scrambled."

Sharp intakes of breath echoed around the inside of the car, as the three women digested what they had been told. The revelation was clearly a surprise to them. It was less so to me. When Uncle Archie first told me of his intention, I did wonder if we were supposed to extend the length of the kite's strings, but I didn't dare question the decision-making. After all, he appeared to know exactly what he was doing.

As my aunts continued to come to terms with the excitement of the last few minutes, I became aware of a different sensation: my nose was starting to react to a strange and very unpleasant smell. And I wasn't alone. Auntie Jessie's sense of smell was also in a heightened state. "Oooh, that's a bit ripe," she said. "Has someone gone and put their foot in something nasty?"

The comment led to a mini witchhunt and soon my aunts had discovered the source of the offending pong. Super sleuth, Auntie Jessie, was the first to let out an almighty howl of protest as she delightedly named and shamed me. "It's Tony! And he's only gone and stepped in a cow pat," she screeched. "His feet are plastered in the stuff. It's little wonder the car now stinks to high heaven."

Quick as a flash, Uncle Archie vaulted out of the driver's seat, quickly extracting himself from the car. "Open the windows, and the smell will quickly go away," he said as he opened my door and ushered me outside. "In the meantime, I'll crack on and sort out the mess."

It took a good ten minutes to rid my training shoes

of the detritus. Thankfully, Uncle Archie found the remains of a bottle of water in the car boot. Vigorous rubbing of the trainers with one of Auntie Maureen's very best tea cloths, supported by the application of liberal amounts of water, eventually eliminated the problem. When he'd finished, both Cheetahs were soaked and unwearable, so Uncle Archie tied them securely to the roof rack, ignoring my protests and claiming the force of moorland wind would dry them a lot more quickly than merely placing them in the boot. When I had been silenced and he was satisfied all was once again in order – and no police, or military vehicles, could be seen lying in wait on the A61 to apprehend us – we got back into the car. Instantly, the engine roared to life.

"That was certainly a picnic I will never forget," said Auntie Kathleen in a deadpan tone of voice. "I dread to think how much it must have cost to scramble two planes to come and check us out?"

Uncle Archie didn't respond. How could he? Auntie Kathleen was well within her rights to say something, and my uncle was probably counting himself fortunate not to be on the receiving end of a more stinging verbal broadside. Perhaps, if it had been anyone else, the rebuke would have been a lot more significant and crushing. But Auntie Kathleen was a gentle soul, and it was not in her nature to be unkind.

"The men in the car need to be on their best behaviour for the rest of the day," she continued. "And that means you will do as you're told, starting with where we're now going because the ladies, who are the clear majority, would like to revert to the original plan. We want to go to Harrogate and have a nice cup of tea at Betty's. We have had all the excitement we need for one day. What's really needed is some Yorkshire tea and a slice of cake, and a walk around some of the shops. And once that's all been done, we can head off to Beverley for our birthday meal."

Not one word of dissent passed Uncle Archie's lips. He listened respectfully to Auntie Kathleen and accepted her instruction without complaint. Only when she appeared satisfied did he press his foot on the accelerator, gently encouraging the Cortina to make its way back onto the main road. As we rejoined the carriageway, Auntie Maureen started to chuckle. At first, it was a quiet release of nervous tension, but soon it became full-scale laughter. As she struggled to contain herself, Maureen and Jessie followed suit. Soon the chuckles turned into full-throated howls and, when it became clear it wasn't going to end anytime soon, myself and Uncle Archie joined in.

"I don't think I will be doing that again anytime soon," said Uncle Archie when the Gothic architecture of Saint Peter's Church in Harrogate came into view and everyone had started to forget the difficulties of the last hour. "I think our days of kite flying are well and truly over, aren't they Tony? It's best we join the tea and cake brigade for the time being."

So we did.

By the time we left the comfort of Betty's plush Parliament Street address, to begin the journey to the equally picturesque Beverley, and a Chinese restaurant located in the shadows of the town's own medieval Minster, the legend of Menwith Hill had gained special status, which meant the story would be retold many times in the years to come. ✳

SIX

A new season offers renewed hope

MUCH TO THE FRUSTRATION OF my friends and family, I am a vocal, life-long supporter of Hull City. I have rejoiced in the good days (there have been a few, but not that many) and wept when the bad times have descended (of which there have been too many). Yet, despite the urging of almost everyone I know to adopt a team like Leicester City (the nearest 'big club' to where I live), I have always found myself drawn to the black and amber of the Tigers. I look out for their results every time they play and, for seven years, I followed them – home and away. During this time, I witnessed some wonderful performances, as well as quite a few stinkers. I have seen them win at Wembley and Wycombe Wanderers, and get walloped at White Hart Lane (home of Tottenham). Yet no matter how many times I have witnessed a painful Tigers defeat, my support has never wavered.

In the late summer of 1977, my excitement knew no bounds, for the football season was about to kick off, and City had a plum opening day home fixture against

Sunderland. Fourteen months earlier, the Black Cats had visited Hull and thumped us by four goals to one. It was a painful afternoon, and the win guaranteed Sunderland promotion to the First Division (albeit they were relegated the following season). Anyone with a football brain was predicting a similar score this time round against one of the clear favourites to lift the title, for the pundits and doomsters had us ear-marked to finish in the bottom three (which meant dropping into the third tier) long before the season had even started. But not me. For I saw myself as being something of a good luck charm for City, as I had never seen them lose.

Shortly before travelling to Auntie Kathleen's, I received a letter from Mac Stone of the Tigers. He wasn't someone who typed correspondence and took down short-hand notes, but a man who was actively involved in the day-to-day running of the club. He was an important part of the management team. A decision-maker, no less. And it wasn't just any kind of letter he sent me, it was a response to an offer I had sent John Kaye, the manager, in July, begging to be considered as a potential replacement for Chris Chilton, the club's revered (and now long retired) centre forward. Even though I was only twelve, I really believed I could do a good job for Hull. I was tall for my age. I was quick. And I could mix it with boys older than me. Unfortunately, Mr Stone didn't share my confidence. His warm reply stated:

Dear Tony,

Many thanks for your recent correspondence about becoming our new centre forward.

It is kind and generous of you to put yourself forward this way. Unfortunately, we must decline, for profes-

sional football doesn't work this way. If we want to sign
you, we will get in touch with you, or your parents,
directly.
Good luck with in fulfilling your footballing dreams,
and I hope you continue to support City.
Yours sincerely, Mac Stone (Club Secretary).

The polite rejection did nothing to affect my passion
for my hometown club. If anything, it just fuelled my
desire to don the number nine shirt one day. My acute lack
of footballing prowess (I would go on to play rugby union
for twenty-eight years) didn't matter one bit. I was confident I could overcome any obstacles put in my way until I
achieved my destiny – to be Chilton's worthy successor. At
the very least, I was determined I would mirror Stuart
Pearson's achievements before he moved to Manchester
United for a transfer fee of two hundred and forty thou-
sand pounds. Until the day I signed my own professional
contract with the club I loved, I would simply turn the
snub into enthusiastic and tangible support, starting with
the upcoming clash against the Wearsiders.

Before I had played my sugar bowl trick on Uncle
Jim, I had asked my Auntie Kathleen and mum if I could
go to the match. They both said 'yes', provided I behaved!
Even though I had strayed off the straight and narrow a
little bit already, there had been no mention of not letting
me make my pilgrimage to Boothferry Park. So my excitement mounted all week, and by the time Saturday arrived,
I could barely contain myself. I was up at the crack of
dawn, still energised after being buzzed by RAF jets. My
bed was made, my room tidied, and I was dressed and at
the scullery table by seven-thirty in the morning, a good
thirty minutes before Auntie Kathleen and Uncle Jim

awoke from their slumber. After downing two bowls of Rice Krispies and benefitting from all that 'snap, crackle and pop', the next six hours passed by slowly. Every ten minutes, or so, I looked at my watch, and as I did so, I could see Uncle Jim, who had recently emerged from the bathroom, getting more irritated as he wiped the sleep from his eyes and tried to read the newspaper.

"The time won't go by any faster just because you want it to," he said to me. "Why don't you read a book, or play with your toy soldiers for a while? The morning will go by a lot quicker if your mind is occupied and you're not just staring into space."

My uncle's words fell on deaf ears. I couldn't stop thinking about the game. I was getting over-excited. I knew it, as did he. The source was the attachment I had to my hometown team and my firm belief City would claim all the points, just as they had done when I last saw them play, against Wolves in October 1976. That day, they ran out victors by two goals to nil. But, if City could beat Sunderland, that really would top everything.

Shortly before one o'clock, Uncle Fred emerged from his room. His grey flat cap was anchored to his head, and his tweed suit looked slightly out of place on a bright summer's day. So, too, did his chequered scarf and the grim expression he was wearing. It certainly didn't look as though he shared my pre-match optimism.

"Aren't you going to wear your City colours?" I asked him as he sat down on the settee for a moment, waiting for me to put my training shoes on, all traces of the previous day's cowpat cleansed and erased.

"Nay, lad. This will do me fine," he said, uttering

several more words than we were all used to hearing. "Quick about it, now. We'd best be off. We've got a bus to catch, and we mustn't be late, I want to make sure I get my usual place on the terraces."

I quickly did double knots in both my shoes and tied my City scarf around my neck. "I am ready, Uncle Fred," I muttered, joy etched all over my face, the kind all football fans have before kick-off. As we were about to leave, Auntie Kathleen suddenly appeared from the back of the house. She smiled warmly, dusting off the self-raising flour that had found its way onto her apron and suspending her baking duties momentarily. "Make sure you take good care of him, Fred," she said. "Don't lose one another, because we don't want to have to get a search party to come out and find you. And make sure you have a good time, win, lose or draw."

"There's only going to be one winner today," I replied. And then we were gone, Uncle Fred set a brisk pace as we marched up the Avenue before turning left onto the Lane. From here, the number thirteen bus stop at Hall Road – from where we would catch a specially chartered supporters bus – was a mere ten minutes away.

Football crowds are like no other large gathering of people. Experience has taught me they are predominantly made up of men, many of whom behave like teenagers when they don't have their wives, or partners, holding their hands. A large number also smoke, drink until they are drunk as skunks, and then talk utter tripe. Funnily enough, I have always found them to be quite comforting and exhilarating company, especially when there are less than a couple of hours to go before kick-off time and the sense of expectation reaches exaggerated heights. This starts from the moment you put your scarf on and jump onto the bus, or into the car that's carrying you to the stadium. So it was that Saturday, as I sat with Uncle Fred on the bus as it slowly made its way down Hull's tree-lined avenues to the hallowed terraces of the Boothferry Park stadium.

Being a man of few words, Uncle Fred barely spoke for the duration of the ride. The most I heard him say was "reet" and "ta" as he swapped some silver-coloured coins with the bus conductor in return for two return tickets. In fairness, he didn't need to speak. I was too busy daydreaming about what was going to happen that afternoon in front of a sixteen thousand-strong crowd on a pitch City fans regarded as the finest playing surface in England. Such was my state of delirium, Uncle Fred had to shake my shoulder to get me to focus on the present as the bus ground to a halt at its ultimate destination. The thirty-minute journey had passed quickly. It was time to make tracks.

"Wake up," he said in a slightly raised voice. "We're here, Tony. There's not long to go now, so follow me, and remember to stay close. Don't forget what your Auntie Kathleen said – she doesn't want you to go missing. And neither do I." And with that, we had climbed down from the bus and were mingling with the large crowd that was gathering on Anlaby Road. Interestingly, none of the fans we were standing alongside were wearing black and amber scarves; theirs were red and white. What's more, we appeared to be in a queue full of men vocally displaying their loyalty to Sunderland, and a handful of them were pointing at me, clenching their fists and shouting words I couldn't comprehend. I looked for Uncle Fred, who had become the *Invisible Man*. At first, I couldn't see him. Then, after subduing the mild panic that was starting to grow within me, I spotted his flat cap. He was about ten feet (that's six men) in front of me, in a long queue that was snaking its way towards... the away end. "Uncle Fred," I called. "Uncle Fred. Uncle Fred!"

All I got out of him was an arm wave and a stern look that said 'be quiet'. So I was, all the way to the turnstile, where I paid my fifty pence admission charge and earned a curious look from the man who took my money. Once inside the ground, I again looked for my uncle. He should have been waiting for me on the other side, but he wasn't there. I looked again. Nope, he was nowhere to be seen. Then I had a brain wave: I remembered where he always stood on the terraces – directly in line with the corner flag, on the top steps (unless it was raining, when he always sought shelter). Sure enough, after picking my way through the massed ranks of opposition supporters, I eventually found him.

"Bloody hell," he whispered as loudly as he dared. "You need to keep it down a bit, Tony. We're surrounded by Sunderland fans. If you don't keep it quiet, they'll lynch both of us and our lifeless corpses will be hung on the floodlights. Now, be a good lad and keep quiet, particularly if we score. No jumping up and down and celebrating. Please, promise me you will do that." Reluctantly I nodded my agreement. But I was confused. Here we were, about to watch City, and my uncle had led me into the den of the foe without any mention of it when we were on the bus. Whatever was going on?

"This isn't the time for questions like that," he blustered when I probed him. "Not right now. The game's about the start. Let's enjoy it, remembering not to get too excited, and I will explain everything when we're on our way home. But you must promise me you won't say a word to Auntie Kathleen or Uncle Jim. Do you understand?" I had little choice but to agree. And as soon as the word 'yes' had passed my lips, an enormous roar echoed around the old ground, as both sets of fans welcomed our respective heroes onto the pitch. In the City team that day were Jeff Wealands and Peter Daniel (two of my favourites), but no Billy Bremner, who was unable to play due to a knee injury he had picked up in the pre-season. I was gutted not to see the Scottish midfield terrier in a Hull shirt that day, but I put my disappointment behind me. Instead, I turned my attention to the events unfolding in front of me and, after squeezing myself in between two large, tattooed visiting supporters, I managed to secure a great view of the clash.

For the entire first half, the game was a complete anti-climax. A promising start petered out into nothingness, with neither side willing to step up the pace. Forty-five minutes passed by uneventfully and slowly. Although we hadn't troubled the visiting goalkeeper, there was at least one major consolation for all home supporters: City weren't trailing by the time the referee's whistle signalled half-time. After becoming wedged between the two Sunderland fans, who I learned by eavesdropping on their conversation were called Eric and Carl, I discovered it was impossible to turn around. I was so tightly wedged in. I looked up pleadingly at Eric, whose left hand had the letters L-O-V-E tattooed near the knuckles while the right hand only had three fingers on which H-A-T had been inked. Presumably an 'E' was on the missing pinkie? I asked politely: "Excuse me, do you mind letting me through so I can go and find my uncle?" As soon as I had finished speaking the man roared with laughter.

"What? Are you telling me there is another imposter in the away end?" he enquired with a degree of menace laced into his thickly accented voice. His beard was discoloured by the stains of tobacco, and he had one large yellow tooth protruding from the top of his mouth. His sarcastic and unfriendly tone instantly put me on a state of high alert. "Tell you what, point out where your uncle is standing and we'll take you directly to him. It would be nice to meet him and have a cosy chat."

I have always had a sixth sense that identifies potential danger. Therefore, I was thankful I didn't have time to point Uncle Fred out to these two men, for no sooner had Eric finished speaking to me, and closed his tight-fitting mouth thereby hiding his solitary tooth than uproar broke out among the Sunderland fans. I looked towards the pitch and quickly saw the source of their agitation: it was a ginger-haired, Sheepskin coat-wearing Hull fan, who had run onto the pitch and was now baiting the visiting supporters. In response, hundreds of proud Wearsiders moved like waves washing up against the seashore. One second I was going forward, the next I was being taken in the opposite direction. It was frightening. It was exciting. All the while it was happening I was desperately trying to identify Uncle Fred's face among the wall of flesh that enveloped me. Throughout the ordeal, all I could hear was a single swear word being repeatedly chanted in unison by the men in red and white, their arms pointed at the lone City fan who dared to strut his stuff in front of them while issuing some sort of primeval combat challenge (albeit the rapidly approaching stewards and police officers ensured he faced minimal danger). As I watched the spectacle unfold, I made a mental note to ask Auntie Kathleen what the word "wan-ker" meant at an appropriate moment. I thought I knew, but it was always good to be sure.

As both teams emerged for the second half, both sets of supporters settled down once again. Regardless of our age, or gender, we were all eager to enjoy the main reason we had all been drawn to Boothferry Park in the first place. In this regard, I was to enjoy a far more profitable after-noon than those from Wearside, albeit it wasn't until the fifty-seventh minute when our bearded Welsh defender, Dave Roberts, broke the deadlock. Three-quarters of Boothferry Park erupted when the ball bounced into the back of the net. Despite my promise to Uncle Fred, I found I couldn't contain myself, and I didn't hold back my jubilation – until my unbridled glee drew some scornful and abusive remarks from those around me.

"What the heck is he doing in here?" someone standing close to me muttered. "He'd bloody well better behave himself, or he'll find himself feeling the back of my hand." The angry words meant nothing to me. I was immune to the threat they carried. All that mattered was my beloved City were in front. We were avenging the four-one drubbing of two seasons earlier in the best possible way. Soon it would get so much better. A second goal was scored seventeen minutes later, again by Roberts (who was not usually a prodigious marksman). This led to Hull fans breaking out into wild celebrations. You'd have thought their horse had won the Grand National. Forgetting where I was, my own jubilation went into overdrive once again. Any inhibitions I had were well and truly cast off. Unable to stomach me any longer, Eric grabbed my tracksuit collar, which I had put on at halftime in a bid to conceal my City shirt and true allegiance, and shook me violently.

"Calm down, or I will clip your flipping ear," he growled, as the thumb and three fingers of his right hand gripped me tightly. "If that doesn't shut you up, I will take you up to the railway line and strap you to it. And you know what'll happen to you when the train leaves, don't you?" As he spat out his threats, Eric turned and pointed at the railway track that ran parallel to the East Stand. He then slowly drew his finger across his throat so I could have no doubts about what he was suggesting. Boothferry Park was the only ground in Britain that had its own siding, which enabled supporters to travel to Paragon Station (the city's main rail connection) and then easily negotiate the last couple of miles by jumping onto one of several match-day specials that ran directly to the stadium. At that moment, I really believed Eric would carry out his threat. I looked at him blankly, the joy of the occasion drained completely from my face. It was the contrition he needed to let me go. As he did, my gaze returned to the turf and the closing minutes of the game.

I made sure I heeded Eric's words, particularly as full-time approached and Hull fired in their third goal to seal the win. I watched on as Bruce Bannister, an acquisition from Plymouth Argyle, turned and saluted the City faithful as the roar of "Tigers! Tigers!" echoed around the stadium. In the away end, there was no such joy. I heard comments like "bloody useless" and "what a bunch of donkeys" mouthed by multiple mouths as hordes of Sunderland fans streamed away from the ground. Among those who beat a hasty retreat were a downcast Eric and Carl.

"Hey, lad. Next time, make sure you go in the sodding home end," shouted Eric, as he made his way to the packed carriages of the matchday train. "If you don't, you might find yourself standing next to fans who are less tolerant than us, and then you'll be in a spot of bother. And your age won't protect you."

I waved and tapped my forehead acknowledging the warning. In truth, I had no right to be among the Sunderland fans as they mourned their side's capitulation. At that moment, I appreciated his frustrations and hurt, not that I cared. As the visitors continued to drift away, large gaps appeared, and that's when I saw Uncle Fred's solitary figure once again. He was a good fifty feet away from me, standing on his own where one of the cast iron pillars, which held up the rusting East Stand roof, was erected. As I walked towards him, he looked up and locked his eyes on me. I knew instantly he wanted me to come no further, a point emphasised when his hand made a subtle 'stop' motion – the second time he had communicated such an instruction that afternoon. I don't know how long I was left there on my own – mere seconds or a couple of minutes – but soon enough the game drew to an end, overjoyed City fans let out an almighty roar, and what remained of the red and white horde trooped off to return to the north-east, their wings well and truly clipped. With the terraces empty, I spied some discarded programmes that had cost their owners the princely sum of twelve pence. I picked up a couple and popped them in my pocket; they would be my own spoils of war, souvenirs that I would look at in the weeks ahead and recall the electricity of this charged afternoon.

"Come on, daft lad," said Uncle Fred, who had ghosted his way to me as I collected the programmes. "We need to have a good chat before we get home, and we need to agree what we're going to tell your Auntie Kathleen and Uncle Jim, don't we?"

Neither of us uttered another word as we walked to the turnstiles, the very ones we had entered a couple of hours earlier. Our silence continued all the way back to the bus stop, where the familiar blue and white colours of the East Yorkshire double-decker and an animated queue awaited us, and that's when Uncle Fred decided to begin what would prove to be a very short discussion.

"Now, Tony," he said in his most earnest of voices. "I really don't want you telling your aunt that you have spent all afternoon in the away end at Boothferry Park. That will not be what she wants to hear. I would really prefer it if we could keep it our little secret."

I nodded, slowly, understanding what he meant. When Uncle Fred spoke again, we had climbed the stairs to the first floor of the bus, which would give us panoramic views of the tightly packed rows of terraced houses that lined the populous avenues of Hull. We had settled nicely in our seats when the bus driver started the engine and all the passengers were momentarily overwhelmed by the powerful, acrid smell of diesel, which flooded the vehicle thanks to all the windows being open. A few choking coughs filled the air as the fumes dispersed and the bus pulled away and made its way through the thick blanket of traffic towards Cottingham. "By all means," he continued, once the journey was well underway, "tell Auntie Kathleen about the great win you've seen this afternoon. That'll keep her happy. You can describe the goals, and even tell her about the bloke who tried to take on all the Sunderland fans at half-time. She'll roll her eyes and have a good laugh at that. But that's all she needs to know, for Auntie Kathleen is like a lot of ladies – she doesn't really understand what football is all about."

Puzzled, I asked: "But Uncle Fred, why did we have to watch the game in the away end? Their fans are really nasty. I nearly got into real trouble. Why didn't we stand with the other Hull supporters?"

A big smile spread across his face. "Sometimes you have to make little sacrifices in life," he explained. "The one I make every time City play at home is to go into the away end, from where I watch the match. I do this not because I want to be in danger. I do it because the away end has the cheapest prices, it's nearest to the bus stop, and it also has the best view of the pitch. I've been standing on the same spot for more years than I care to remember, and have never had any bother. Today is the nearest I have ever come to trouble, and that was only because you nearly gave the game away. But we won't dwell on that. I'm sure, if you don't fully understand what I'm saying right now, you will sometime soon."

Even at my tender age, Uncle Fred's logic left me baffled. And then I remembered it was the rationale of a man who had once mixed paraffin with two-stroke petrol over a naked flame. Suddenly I found this kind of logic amusing and reassuring, understanding now why my family constantly referred to his 'special' status. Thereafter, any confusion I had quickly evaporated and I thoroughly enjoyed the trip back to Auntie Kathleen's house, not least because Uncle Fred was more animated and talkative than he had ever been when in my company. And so he should have been: we had enjoyed an eventful afternoon watching our team secure a handsome and very unexpected victory.

It is a Saturday I will remember for a long time, not least because it was the day I pledged, on a rickety old bus, that no matter how many Hull games I attended in the future, I would never again follow my Uncle Fred (or anyone else, for that matter) into the away end at Boothferry Park.

SEVEN

The forgiving war heroes

THE STORY OF JOZEF PODBIERESKI and his wife, Zofia, is one to give hope to anyone who hears it. This remarkable couple survived the German invasion of their Polish homeland in 1939 – refusing to yield to nazi terror and oppression. Zofia spent several years incarcerated in concentration camps, while Jozef enlisted as a soldier and fought for the allies, becoming one of the incredibly brave souls who worked in Occupied France with the Resistance, frustrating the German war effort by putting their own lives at risk on a daily basis. During those hazardous and treacherous days, it is fair to say that whatever they witnessed was as close to hell as anyone can possibly imagine.

Quiet, softly-spoken and incredibly hardworking, the war years forced the Podbiereski's to endure a long period of enforced separation before they were reunited by the Red Cross after the Second World War had ended – when it's likely both had given up all hope of ever finding one another again. It was in the north of England that fate intervened and Jozef and Zofia saw one another again at a special camp for Polish people in Willerby (located on the outskirts of Hull). Displaced people from Eastern Europe were relocated throughout the length and breadth of Britain in those early post-war years, and in a bid to ensure ravaged, economically challenged cities (and industries) got access to people with the requisite skills, they would join the settlers who found their way to Cottingham, eventually buying a house and two acres of land on the corner of the Lane and the Avenue. From here, they established a successful market garden business and integrated themselves, and their daughter, Kazia, into everyday village life.

Throughout my childhood, I had known nothing about the incredible Podbiereksi story. I was completely unaware of the trials and tribulations experienced by 'Mr Joe' (the name we all used when speaking to him) and Zofia (pronounced Sofia), and of the events that had defined much of their early life. They were simply neighbours who happened to come from a foreign country. For a child like me, that was as complicated as it got. I often saw them, waved and said "hello", exchanging pleasantries as I stood in the rear gardens of number seven and number thirteen. Just like my grandad and uncles, Mr Joe would always be found wearing an obligatory flat cap in all weathers, while his wife always seemed to have a scarf wrapped around her head. Both were permanently bronzed – even during winter – and they always seemed to have a dusty pair of wellies on their feet. But nothing they did, or said, ever suggested they had lived through such hardships. I occasionally heard members of my family refer to the couple, but because the conversation was usually about something to do with vegetables or flowers, I tended to stop listening. Yet whenever my family talked about them, something I now recognise as the deepest of respect was always present. Alas, in 1977, when I was care-free and callow, I clearly recall displaying far less of this trait than my elders would have liked.

One such occasion was on Monday, the twenty-second day of August. The date was significant because it meant I had passed the midway point of my already event-ful holiday. I had blotted my copybook with my 'adventur-ous' behaviour (thankfully the lemonade bottle escapade was not yet known about by Auntie Kathleen and Uncle Jim) but I hadn't been in the dog house for too long. Recalling the experience of being pursued by RAF fighter planes, we had spent the weekend imagining we had become some of the country's most wanted fugitives – and we laughed at the thought of being notorious. But it was only funny for a while, soon becoming boring. By Monday, I had become a bit of a stuck record, telling anyone who would listen about City's heroics against Sunderland. I had sorely tested the patience of Auntie Kathleen and Uncle Jim, and despite their best efforts, they couldn't find a way of shutting me up. The one person who wouldn't want to have her senses assaulted was my mum, as I discovered when she phoned during her lunchtime to see what I had been up to. When she asked, I told her all about the excite-ment of my Saturday afternoon, and it wasn't very long before I heard her yawning down the phone. Had I not been so unobservant, I would have quickly realised she was losing the will to live. "That's all very interesting," she commented after finding an opportune moment to break through my monologue. "Make sure you enjoy the rest of the week and continue to be a good lad for your Auntie Kathleen. I will see you in a few days when we can have a good chat about everything you have been up to. Now, pass me over to your aunt – and make sure you continue to be a good lad."

With Auntie Kathleen becoming absorbed in her conversation with mum, I opted to take Sweep for a walk. I needed to get some fresh air. After finding his lead, I woke him up from his lair under the table, and then proceeded to take the uncooperative hound on a forced march around the block – the same two-mile trek Uncle Jim undertook every evening. This time, however, I made sure he was kept well away from any other dogs and their owners, for I really didn't want a repeat of the King Charles Spaniel episode of the previous Thursday. When we were on the home straight and had passed Elliott's, Sweep had a surge of uncharacteristic energy, tugged at his leash, and completely caught me by surprise. Before I knew what had happened, the cunning canine had freed himself from my grip and was bolting in the general direction of the Avenue. I chased after him for more than a hundred yards, but the mutt could run like the clappers when he wanted to, and he held a strong advantage over me. With his legs pumping like pistons, the chains of his lead bouncing off the pavement, and his large ears dancing in the gentle summer breeze, the distance between us grew. In the end, I gave up. The last thing I saw was him swerving to avoid Auntie Bess (a neighbour who lived at number five) as she rounded the corner. Clearly surprised to see Sweep's ungainly frame bearing down on her, she produced a deft side-step, retaining her composure rather well as she did so, albeit I suspect her heart momentarily skipped a couple of beats. "Don't worry, love, he does that all the time," she said in between a handful of large gasps of breath that served to steady her slightly frayed nerves. "I am forever seeing your Uncle Jim running home, trying to get control of him before your Auntie Kathleen finds out. That dog has escaped more times than Houdini."

After bidding me a good day, Auntie Bess continued her brisk walk up the Lane. As I watched her make steady progress on the recently resurfaced path, I noticed something sticking out of the lush green hawthorn bush that shielded the land owned by Mr Joe and Zofia from the hustle and bustle of the main road. It was a blackened object, thin and rounded, invisible to the eye unless you were standing at a certain angle, as I was. The protruding object was at least a foot in length, as I discovered when I carefully extracted it from the foliage and gave it a cursory inspection. A sense of disappointment replaced my excitement as I quickly realised it was merely an old iron railing, the type used to fence and protect churches, schools, and a wide range of public buildings. From far away, it had looked interesting, something of real interest. But after realising what it was, I had little use for it. So, I threw it back into the hedgerow.

And that reckless act proved to be my next undoing.

No sooner had I thrown the rod back into the hedge than I heard the unmistakable sound of breaking glass as the rod smashed into one of the hidden greenhouses located behind the hawthorn hedge. It took a few seconds for me to comprehend what had happened, and the realisation I had caused unintentional, potentially serious damage, left me feeling confused and fearful. There had been no desire on my part to cause more trouble All I had tried to do was return the bar from whence it had come. My mistake was to put too much effort into things because rather than nestle once again in the thick of the hedge, it had sliced through the foliage, shattering several sheets of glass on the other side. At that moment, I once again recalled my mum stressing to me the importance of owning up whenever I did something wrong. But my track record during the past week had not been good, so I fled the scene as quickly as my legs would allow. It didn't take me long to make it back to number thirteen, albeit my lungs were close to bursting. Without hesitating, I opened the back door, startling Auntie Kathleen, who was sitting down at the scullery table drinking a cup of tea. Beyond her, I saw the smug and distinctive face of Sweep, who was looking directly at me, his eyes full of contempt. He had only been home for a handful of minutes and was finishing off the Winalot biscuits that always awaited his safe return. Occasionally he averted his gaze so he could gulp down large mouthfuls of water, spilling as much on the floor tiles as went into his mouth. But he made sure he looked up every few seconds, just to see how I was reacting. Thankfully, I didn't have to put up for too long with the feelings of humiliation that enveloped me.

"What on earth is the matter?" enquired my surprised aunt after I had burst through the door. "Spill the beans, Tony, as there is clearly something wrong. And I am not talking about Sweep giving you the slip."

There and then, part of me wanted to confess everything. But my inner demon, the type that afflicted many boys of a certain age, chose that moment to whisper in my ear, insisting I said nothing about the incident. "Sorry, I didn't mean to startle you," I said, the dark side winning that particular duel. "I was worried about Sweep. He got away from me just around the corner, and I was frightened he may not have come home. Thankfully, I can see he had no trouble getting back to the house. But I am really sorry I couldn't control him. He caught me completely by surprise." Auntie Kathleen's response was to roll her eyes and smile. "I know. I know," she said. "Uncle Jim is always dashing home, getting in to a right old state because he thinks something has happened to him. But it never has, and it hopefully never will. Sweep's a wily dog who can sense the exact moment when your concentration is at its lowest point. That's when he takes control and makes his bid for freedom, and once he's got it, all he does is trot back here, bark at the door and demand to be let in and fed. He loves his occasional victory and his home comforts."

The comment enabled a sense of relief to start pulsing through me. I laughed. Just as I started to relax, Auntie Kathleen and I nearly jumped out of our skins. There was a loud rapping noise at the front door, and it was the kind of hammering nobody ignored. "Whoever could that be?" she inquired. "They are making enough noise to awaken the dead. Whatever could be so important?"

As an aside, she added: "And it had better not be about something you have got up to!"

As she rose from her chair and made her way to the front of the house, I felt a sinking feeling. I was pretty sure I knew who might be at the door. Sure enough, I didn't have long to wait before Mr Joe's distinctive voice reached me – and I could tell he was in an agitated mood. In heavily accented English, I could make out the words "broken", "iron bar", "vandalism" and "unacceptable". An awkward moment of silence ensued, followed by my Auntie Kathleen apologising profusely. After a couple of minutes, the conversation seemed to be over as Mr Joe said "tak" and left the house. After a brief pause, when time seemed to stand still, Auntie Kathleen was suddenly sitting once again at the table with an expression and body language that had completely changed.

"I have just had a very interesting conversation with Mr Joe, and I think you need to explain yourself," she said, before drinking what was left of her tea and letting her all-knowing eyes lock onto me once again. "That poor man. He is not happy, and he has every reason to be upset. I don't know why you have done what you have, but you will need to offer him something more than a mealy-mouthed explanation when you tell him why you have just gone and inexplicably damaged one of his greenhouses."

Auntie Kathleen's words hung in the air. When I sensed the time was right, I attempted to explain what had happened. I had only just started talking when Auntie Kathleen lost patience with me. "Enough, enough," she hissed. "You need to grow up. You are coming with me right now, and you're going to tell Mr Joe yourself what happened, and how sorry you are for breaking his property. And you will accept whatever punishment he deems appropriate, because you need to learn your lesson, Tony. You really do."

My head was spinning. I was surprised at how quickly my day had spiralled out of control. I started to think I must be jinxed (whatever that was). Before I could rehearse what I was going say to the Podbiereskis, I found myself being dragged by the arm. Auntie Kathleen's vice-like grip quickly hauled me outside, and I found myself walking up the Avenue, towards Mr Joe's and Zofia's, where my judge and jury awaited.

"I think I understand what you are saying," said Mr Joe, after he had listened to my explanation and mulled things over. "So, there was no intention on your part to cause us any harm, or destroy anything? The glass-breaking was a freak accident? You are telling us you expect us to believe this was just an accident?"

I had stood at the front door of the Podbiereskis, on the 'naughty step' as my mum liked to call it, for a full ten minutes. Only after Auntie Kathleen had pleaded my case was I allowed in. Then I had to repeatedly explain myself to ensure there were no inconsistencies in my version of the events that had led to two panes of glass being broken. I couldn't work out whether anyone believed me, as the expressions of Mr Joe, Zofia and Auntie Kathleen remained neutral. It felt like I was standing in the dock of the Old Bailey, not knowing if the judge was going to pass the death sentence, or not. As all three adults appeared less and less convinced by my pleas of innocence, the more desperate I became. In the end, after a lengthy period had lapsed, Auntie Kathleen acted decisively. "We don't seem to be getting very far," she observed. "Please accept my apologies for any distress caused by this unfortunate incident. I am sure Tony meant no harm to either of you. By the sounds of it, the whole thing was an accident caused by Tony not engaging his brain, and he has form in this regard. That doesn't mean he will escape punishment, for he will get short shrift from his mum once I have told her about what's happened today. And he will obviously make good here by paying for the damage out of his own pocket money."

I winced. The cost of replacing the window panes was more than two pounds. The prospect of losing some of my own money hadn't been discussed, and to hear it being offered was a shock. Knowing I was likely to lose the money mum had given for my second week would test the sincerity of any apology I would be asked to offer, for I was doing all I could to save enough to be able to buy a rugby ball. I spent a moment thinking about the Mitre all-weather size-five I had set my heart on. Just as a fully-blown self-pity party threatened to consume me, I realised I was in the wrong and needed to atone for my mistake. The rugby ball would have to wait.

As I looked at the adults, I could see Mr Joe nodding his head in appreciation of Auntie Kathleen's diplomatic skills. He said nothing but looked as though he was deciding what to do next. Eventually, Mr Joe looked directly at me and said: "I accept your apology, young man. But you were extremely foolish to run away. Fleeing the scene makes you look guilty. If it was an accident, why would you do that?"

Before I could answer, he continued: "Let's not dwell on this. To put things to rest, I suggest you come here tomorrow morning, at eight o'clock sharp, and work with me and Mrs Podbiereski in the greenhouse. You can help us repair the glass, tidy up the hedge and do some general jobs around the place. After all, there are always plenty of things to do in a market garden like ours. And when you have spent the day working hard, any debt you owe us will have been repaid. There will be no need for you to pay us any of your money."

I was delighted by Mr Joe's words, which meant my rugby ball ambitions remained intact. But before I could say anything, Auntie Kathleen spoke up for us both. "That is very fair and very kind of you," she said. "Tony will be very happy to come around and lend a hand, and I will make sure he is with you just after he's had his breakfast. One again, please accept our apologies."

A smile passed across the mouths of the Podbiereskis and once again I heard Mr Joe utter the word "tak", which I now know means "yes" in his native tongue. Unsure of what to do next, I was grateful when I felt Auntie Kathleen's hand once again take a gentle hold of my arm and guide me back towards the Avenue.

"You are a very lucky young man to have got off so lightly," she said as we walked the short distance to number thirteen. "Mr Joe could have come down on you like a ton of bricks. Do you realise Zofia was in the greenhouse when your act of foolishness led to the glass being smashed? It gave her quite a fright. You are a lucky so-and-so. Now, just make sure you do everything Mr Joe and Zofia ask of you. Create a good impression, and we can quickly move on. But if you don't learn from this, then your mum will have to become involved, and we both know she will be a lot less lenient than me. Do we understand one another?"

I did. I knew my mum had been having a hard time, and the last thing she needed was to find out I had been getting myself into trouble. She needed a break, and if she found out I had been up to no good, she wouldn't get one. It was as simple as that.

"Don't worry, Auntie Kathleen, I will be on my very best behaviour," I pledged. "I won't let you, or mum, down. And I will do everything Mr Joe asks of me."

In truth, I was dreading what the following day would bring. The last thing I wanted to do was work. I'd never had to do hard work in my life, so the thought of having to get my hands dirty and do manual work – for eight long hours – was not something I was looking forward to. On the other hand, I did accept I must be punished.

"Okay," she said after a while. "Let's try and finish the day off on a positive note. I promise not to say anything about this to Uncle Jim, or your mum, if you volunteer to do the washing up tonight, after we have had dinner. And, if you do so, you will get into Uncle Jim's good books, as he will be able to relax after a long day at work. What do you say, have we got a deal?"

The smile returned to her face. Auntie Kathleen didnot do misery and despair for long. "Have I told you we are going to be having Toad in the Hole and onion gravy, followed by one of my home-made rice puddings?" she asked. "I am sure there will be seconds for you, just as long as I can count on you helping me to get everything sorted out?" My aunt had a special talent for putting people at ease, and today, even though I had caused her more distress, I was the one to benefit from her special treatment. It was easy to understand why everyone in my family loved her so much.

"I will try to be on my best behaviour," I pledged.

Seemingly satisfied, Auntie Kathleen opened the back door of number thirteen, just in time to hear a blood-curdling howl escape from the depths of Sweep's throat, as he awoke from yet another deep sleep.

"Now there's a welcome you don't get very often," observed my aunt. "It might sound like one of the Hounds of the Baskervilles is about to go berserk, but I know he's just pleased to see us. Go and give him a good stroke, Tony, and I'll start making the tea." ✳

EIGHT

Punching above my weight

BY FIVE O'CLOCK THE FOLLOWING day, just about every bone in my body seemed to ache. As decreed less than twenty-four hours earlier, I had served my penance, completing a full shift for Mr Joe and Zofia. Under their watchful eyes, holes aplenty had been dug, plants watered, vegetation had been moved from one greenhouse to another, and I had played the part of a willing dogsbody to near perfection. I only moaned once throughout the whole day and, even then, the Podbiereskis chose to pretend they had not heard my complaints, which ceased after a few minutes and doused the few flames that had flared from my bonfire of self-pity.

By the time the working day drew to an end, I found, rather surprisingly, that I had enjoyed my first real taste of work – not least, because the Podbiereskis had treated me kindly. I had been dreading my punishment (or "the cleansing of the slate" as Auntie Kathleen described it), but it couldn't have been more different than the unfriendly experience I had expected. The notion I would be worked like a dog (my understanding of what manual work was all about) wasn't lost on me; it taught me a lot about myself – particularly the way I perceived and judged so much around me.

As I said my goodbyes and made to leave the main greenhouse, Mr Joe took me to one side. When he was sure we were out of earshot of Zofia, who, I observed, worked as hard as any man I knew, he said: "I hope your punishment has not been too difficult for you? We have tried to make things as interesting as possible, albeit this is a physical job and there aren't many corners that can be cut. But I have watched you throughout the day, and you have not shirked the jobs you have been asked to do. So, consider any debt fully repaid. We will never speak of the broken glass again, and I will also make sure to tell your aunt what a good worker you have been."

Mr Joe fell silent. He was waiting for a response. As I remained mute – silenced by my embarrassment at being praised – I could feel him watching me. As he did so, I remained unsure of how I should respond. I really didn't know whether a 'thank you' or another 'sorry' was appropriate. Sensing my discomfort and awkwardness, as he had throughout much of the day, Mr Joe took control of the situation: he stretched out his giant right fist – a move that caught me completely off-guard. After waiting a few seconds for me to offer my own, much smaller paw, only for it to stay firmly by my side, he asked: "Have you never shaken the hand of another man, Tony?"

It was a question I could only answer one way. "No," I replied. "Never."

Mr Joe simply sighed and shook his head when he heard my response. As I looked at several boxes of tomatoes I had helped to pick, I heard him utter the word "tak" yet again as he once extended his hand a second time. Without hesitation, I accepted his new invitation. I regretted it instantly, as my fingers felt like they were being crushed by the vice-like grip of this kindly man. When he saw my expression, he couldn't contain himself; laughter – loud and carefree – punctuated the stillness of the early evening. "My goodness, I am so sorry," he said when he saw I was suffering physical discomfort. "I hope I haven't hurt you? I just wanted to shake your hand to say 'thank you' for your efforts. It's what men do when there is mutual respect between one another. Today, you have earned my respect. You can now tell your aunt that all is well between us, and when I see her I promise I will do likewise. Hopefully, that may help you get back into her good books. Now, be on your way, have a good evening, and make sure you don't push any more iron railings through my hedge."

Still not used to being spoken to so openly, I mumbled a muffled "thank you" and "goodbye" before briskly walking out of the greenhouse and striding purposefully back to number thirteen. As I paced the short distance, I reflected (as much as a twelve-year-old can do) on the many things said to me by Mr Joe and Zofia throughout the last few hours, particularly the importance of having a good work ethos. My mum had often told me I was a "layabout", and her words went largely ignored by me. But she was right.

Unusually for me, I remained quiet and reflective for much of teatime, steadfastly refusing to be seduced by Auntie Kathleen and Uncle Jim's concerted attempts to get me to tell them about the day. Even that evening's fry-up (several rashers of smoked bacon, a couple of sausages, a runny egg and a portion of chips, the height of which dominated the plate and rivalled K2) couldn't break me down. For something about the Podbiereskis and their way of living had touched me deep within.

Teatime came and went, and so, too, did the washing up, with Uncle Jim taking command. I picked up the tea towel and ensured crockery and cutlery were returned to their allotted homes all sparkling and clean.

By six-thirty, everything was in order and my aunt and uncle had decided to settle down in front of the telly to watch that evening's edition of *Calendar* on Yorkshire TV. They beckoned me to join them, indicating the settee was free. I walked over and sat down, and it was at that moment I was brutally assaulted by the foulest of unnatural smells. My eyes darted from side to side, but it was clear I was the only person to have detected the toxic smell that was about to pollute our air. I looked sideways, and there, by Uncle Jim's feet, I found the source: Sweep was looking as proud as any dog could be after releasing an odour into the atmosphere as lethal as any nerve agent being developed by Russian, American or British military scientists.

"Oh, my goodness, what in heaven's name is that?" shrieked Auntie Kathleen, as her senses were suddenly assaulted by the violent methane maelstrom. A look of complete bewilderment was etched on her face as she scanned the room, her eyes desperately seeking out the guilty party before settling on her over-loved and over-fed pooch, whose tail was beating the floor, the way a Zulu warrior thumps his shield on the field of battle. "You are a bad lad," continued my aunt, once she was convinced of Sweep's guilt. "That is disgraceful, and it's certainly not something you do inside the house." Looking directly at my uncle, she added: "Jim, you'll have to take him for a walk. He must need the loo. That can be the only reason he smells so bad. So, you need to go. Right now."

Uncle Jim, who remained immune to the overpowering strength of Sweep's bodily contribution, looked perplexed and motioned in a way that suggested he was about to protest. But as his lips twitched, and it seemed he might say something, the smell finally reached him and he started to reel and splutter. "What the heck has he been eating?" asked my bewildered uncle in-between coughs as he quickly rose from his chair. Then talking directly to the dog, he added: "You should be holding your head in shame. That is no way to behave inside the home, so let's get you outside and exercised. Hopefully, the walk will get rid of whatever has caused that godawful stink."

Within moments, Uncle Jim's jacket was on, his cap was tilted at a jaunty angle on his forehead, the dog's collar had been clipped onto the leash, and Sweep was being dragged bodily towards the back door, from where his under-exercised legs would be subjected to an unwelcome bout of exercise. "C'mon," said Uncle Jim encouragingly, trying his best to coax the mutt out of the house. "You only have yourself to blame. So, let's get going, and there had better be no slipping of your chain this evening, if you don't mind."

The back door made a creaking noise as it was opened and closed, and soon human and canine footsteps could be heard echoing off the Avenue's tarmac pavement. As they faded away, Auntie Kathleen clapped her hands. "Oh, I nearly died when I caught that smell in my nostrils," she roared in my direction as she struggled to contain herself. "Wasn't it disgusting? That animal had better not do one of those again in the near future or I'll send him on a one-way trip to the vets. You mark my words. Now. As Uncle Jim is going to be out for the next forty minutes, how about you tell me all there is to say about today's events with Mr Joe and Zofia."

It wasn't a question, more an order, and as soon as she had finished speaking, Auntie Kathleen stood up abruptly, went to the telly and switched off Richard Whitely, who was reporting on the latest developments at the Humber Bridge construction site. With the box now silent, and my aunt sitting comfortably once again in her chair, I had no option but to tell her all about my day with the Podbiereskis.

"That's lovely," she said after I had recounted my time with Mr Joe and Zofia to her complete satisfaction. "They are lovely people. They have been very understanding. So, I think that is all behind us. Now, what are you going to do this evening, because I doubt whether the TV news or *Dad's Army* are your cup of tea?"

I shrugged my shoulders. "Perhaps I will go out for a walk and see if the lads around the corner want to do something. There's bound to be someone out there."

An approving noise from Auntie Kathleen signalled she was happy with my suggestion, and as she settled down for the evening, she gave me a long, lingering look before saying: "Don't you be out any longer than nine o'clock, and make sure you stay out of mischief. We need a few days of peace, so your uncle and I don't jump out of our skins every time there is a knock at the front door."

Although her words were said kindly, my beloved aunt was giving an implicit instruction: I would be skating on thin ice if I got into any more trouble!

The Avenue was basking in the evening sunshine as I walked up to the junction which joined seamlessly with the Lane. Unknown to me at that moment, I was again being propelled towards another act of unintentional infamy, which didn't take long to unravel in a way I was not expecting.

Three minutes after leaving number thirteen, and having walked less than two hundred yards, I walked head-long into a fresh bout of trouble, and it all kicked off after I heard a familiar voice bellow: "Hey, Yorkie, where do you think you are going?"

I tensed and looked up. It was the voice of Paul Sidebottom, who was gesticulating animatedly in my direction in a bid to gain my attention. His brother, Ian, was standing next to him, as was Shaun Goadby. None of them looked pleased to see me as they congregated around a Silver Birch tree in the open field that ran along the far side of Inglemire Lane, all the way to the Jacksons meat processing factory. I hadn't seen this trio since the lemon-ade bottle incident at Elliott's a few days earlier. There's an old saying that 'absence makes the heart grow fonder', however, these particular youths certainly didn't appear to be pleased to see me as I ambled up the road.

"Got anyone into trouble recently, eh?" baited the older Sidebottom. "I can't believe you've dared to show your face round here after all the grief you caused us the other day. I don't know if you realise but, somehow, our dad found out about things, and we got a right walloping that night."

The painful memory seemed to inflame him and Sidebottom, two years my senior, inched forward. His fists were clenched and his face wore a grim expression. After my experiences in Leicestershire, where I was regularly caught up in fights with older boys, I knew what to expect. But before he got close enough to throw his first punch, I tried placating him. "I am sorry it all went wrong," I said, meaning every word. "I should never have talked you all into it. But I can't do anything about what has happened. All I can do is say sorry."

My words fell on deaf ears. Sidebottom continued to edge towards me and judging by his body language he was confident he was going to be successful in the imminent confrontation. He was buoyed by the support shown to him by his brother and neighbour, who called me names that questioned my parentage. Their words stung but strengthened my resolve, and I certainly wasn't going to wait for him to take charge and beat me. Convinced he would soon throw the first shot, I got my blow in first, my quick righthand jab catching Paul smack in the mouth. He looked shocked and immediately stopped his advance. I could see a large dollop of doubt was now painted onto his features. Having learned that surprise is a great advantage in any fight, I followed up my first strike by landing a harder and quicker punch that caught him in exactly the same spot – smack on the mouth. He rocked back on his heels before suddenly dropping to his knees, where he stayed for several seconds staring at the ground and holding his face. His two sidekicks were caught off-guard and they quickly rallied around their fallen man. As I watched, I thought I detected the sound of Paul Sidebottom crying quietly.

"Are you okay," asked his concerned brother. There was no response. "Speak to me, Paul," he pleaded. "Are you alright?"

As I remained in a heightened state of alert, I found

myself ready to face the flurry of punches that must surely come, not just from Paul, but possibly Ian and Shaun,
too. Yet my fears proved groundless, for it soon became
apparent Sidebottom was defeated. His sobs became louder replacing the over-confident growls of moments earlier,
while blood started to ooze from his wounded mouth.
Anxious glances between Ian and Shaun told me it was
time to leave the scene.

"You're an absolute bastard," shouted Ian, as I
walked away and he put an arm around his brother, lead-
ing him towards the family home on the other side of the
Lane. "You wait. Our dad will have you for this."

Panic gripped me as I walked briskly in the opposite
direction to my adversaries, turning left into Keswick
Gardens. As I ate up the yards, I tried to understand how
matters had descended into violence and chaos; and why
trouble seemed to stalk me? In the end, as I found myself
pacing through the nearby allotments and back into the
bottom of the Avenue, it dawned on me that I wasn't to
blame on this particular occasion. As soon as I had been
spotted, a confrontation was always going to be the outcome. The resentment that existed over the bottle fiasco
was simply too great. A clash was inevitable, it was just a
matter of 'when' not 'if'. While this knowledge made me
feel slightly better, I also understood life would now be a lot
harder while I stayed at Auntie Kathleen's, as the locals
might all want to test themselves against the kid who had
downed one of their own.

As I opened the gate to the path that led to number
thirteen, my heart sank. Yet another problem was about to
descend on my aunt and uncle. I decided I must try and
come up with a convincing explanation. Convinced I had

done nothing wrong, just defend myself, I made my way into the back garden, perching on the step immediately outside the back door where I mulled over the events of the last half an hour. I had been sitting there for just a few minutes when I became aware of an almighty commotion at the front of the house. Someone was banging loudly on the front door – and, judging by the beating it was taking, I was in no doubt another complaint was about to be lodged, courtesy of Paul Sidebottom's furious dad.

"Where is he?" demanded an angry Mr Sidebottom, when Uncle Jim eventually opened the front door. "Where is that bloody nephew of yours? If you don't mind, I would like to have a few choice words with him."

Caught by surprise, my uncle struggled to speak coherently. "He's… he's… he's not here. Tony's out," he replied. "Whatever is the matter? What has he now gone and done?"

The response was immediate and savage.

"What has he done?" I heard Mr Sidebottom shout. "He's only gone and knocked my son's two front teeth out in a completely unprovoked attack. There is blood everywhere and a whopping great gap in his mouth. We're not sure anything can be done to fix things. You can be sure I will be taking things further. You mark my words. I intend to make sure your nephew gets his comeuppance."

I was taken aback at the revelation my two punches had left such severe damage. And if I was rocked, then it's little wonder Uncle Jim was rattled by the confrontation. As he got to grips with everything, I heard him call inside to Auntie Kathleen and tell her what was being threatened. It wasn't long before I heard her soothing voice, as she did all she could to take the level of threat – down a notch.

"You can come in and wait, if you like, while Jim goes out and tries to find Tony?" she said to the aggrieved complainant. "Once he is back here, I am sure we can quickly find out what happened and get things sorted. But it is most unlike him to get into trouble of this nature."

Mr Sidebottom rejected her offer immediately. "Your nephew is trouble," he said. "What he has done to my son is totally unacceptable. He's gone up to him and beaten him up. There was no provocation. Nothing. What kind of child does that?"

With his shouts drawing curious looks from neighbours, and his mood darkening, Mr Sidebottom stormed off into the night, leaving a startled Auntie Kathleen and Uncle Jim to close the front door and return to their chairs on either side of the fireplace. As they did, my aunt turned off the early evening delights of Arthur Lowe, John le Mesurier and Clive Dunn, so that an eerie silence descended on the sitting room. The only noise that could be heard was Joey the budgie chirping in his cage, and even his efforts were half-hearted. Eventually, he too quietened. If the cast of Dad's Army had been silenced then you knew matters were serious at number thirteen. After a while, I heard their two voices speaking in hushed tones, but I was unable to follow what was being said. Nonetheless, I was certain my name was mud, and I feared there would now be some severe consequences.

The next five minutes passed slowly. I tried to stand and enter the house, but found I couldn't. I feared what awaited me. Soon I had been waiting in the backyard for half an hour. Inside, the telly had still not been turned on again. Despite my own anxieties, I realised it was time to face the music. As I turned the door handle and walked into the scullery, I was confronted with a deafening silence. It was unnerving. Number thirteen was a house usually filled with happiness, not tension. I tip-toed forward, trying to discover what awaited me, dreading being confronted by my aunt and uncle, people I loved and given more than enough headaches since my arrival. It was a stark fact I hadn't really pondered until that moment. But as the lightbulb was switched on in my head, the peace that claimed the house was shattered.

"So, Muhammad Ali has returned at last," shouted Uncle Jim as I continued my stealthy advance. "I know you are in the scullery, Tony, so let's not pretend you're not in there. According to one of our neighbours, who has just beaten down our front door and threatened us with all sorts of things, you have just assaulted his son, knocking out his two front teeth in the process. Whatever the reason, that kind of behaviour is totally unacceptable. Whatever are you going to do next, Tony – rob a bank, kill someone, lead a coup? More importantly, your aunt and I would like to know when all this trouble is going to end?"

As I came into their view, I sighed and tried my best to explain what had happened – how events had unfolded and spiralled out of control very quickly. But my words counted for nought. Uncle Jim was simply not in the mood to listen to my protestations.

"By buggery, you seem to be a total, bloody liability," he raged. "Your poor mum. Does she have to put up with all of this rubbish in Leicestershire? If she does, she's got my utmost sympathy. You seem to be out of control. If I had my way, you'd be on the receiving end of a damn good hiding right now and we'd then be sending you back home as soon as we bloody well could. But that doesn't appear to be what will happen. Thank your lucky stars you have got Auntie Kathleen in your corner. For some inexplicable reason she seems to believe there is a good reason why all this has happened tonight. In her mind, there is a plausible explanation that sheds some light on how a poor young lad had his teeth knocked out. I just hope for all our sakes, she is right."

The exertion had an immediate impact on Uncle Jim, bringing on one of his regular coughing fits, which quickly saw him retreat to the downstairs toilet. From here, he spent the next few minutes trying to master the condition that was increasingly being controlled by his craving for Embassy No6 cigarettes. Once I was alone with Auntie Kathleen, I attempted to tell my side of the events. Before I had explained things fully, and with Uncle Jim's cough providing a percussive background, she held up her hand. She was commanding my absolute silence.

"Enough. Enough. Enough," she said. "I think it would be a good idea if you went and visited your Auntie Maureen. She's on her own tonight, as Uncle Archie is working a night shift. Baby Emma will now be in bed, and I promised you would pop over the road and spend some time with her. To be honest, a bit of space between you and your Uncle Jim might be a good thing right now, for he needs to calm down. And he won't do if you are in the front room all evening. So, can I trust you to walk across the street and spend the night with your aunt without getting into any more scrapes? We can talk about the fight tomorrow, or some other time, ideally when we've all regained our senses and calmed down."

Auntie Kathleen's suggestion was met with my utmost approval. After quickly washing my hands (Paul

Sidebottom's teeth had left a gash in my right knuckle), I bounded out of the back door and raced over to number sixteen. I rang the doorbell, waited the obligatory three seconds before trying the handle, and, finding the door open, made my way into the house of Campbell, where I found Auntie Maureen soundly asleep, snoring gently on the settee. Mac the dog was curled up at her feet, and his brown eyes sparkled when he saw me.

"Good grief," exclaimed a surprised Auntie Maureen, as she awoke from her slumber to find I had invaded her sitting room. "I nearly jumped out of my skin when I saw you, Tony. I was just dozing after putting Emma up to bed. I hope you haven't been standing there too long?"

It was a rhetorical question that didn't need a reply. As I made myself comfortable on a chair next to Mac, my aunt stretched her arms and rubbed her eyes, which returned her to a full state of high alert. Soon the woes of the evening were forgotten as we became involved in an animated conversation about the events that had led up to my clash with Paul Sidebottom.

"You did what?" she said incredulously, her voice laced with disbelief when I told her how I had given him a good hiding. "I can't believe you knocked out his teeth."

Auntie Maureen was a rebel and a fighter. She always had been – and her auburn hair was an accurate indicator of her temperament. But despite her strong character, at that precise moment, she genuinely looked shocked by my news. "Isn't he a lot older than you?" she asked after coming to terms with my revelation. "And you say he was going to hit you, so you made sure you got in your shot first. Is that right?"

I nodded, the motion answering both questions in an instant.

"I see," she continued. "And his dad was really mad, was he, threatening to throw the kitchen sink at you, Auntie Kathleen and Uncle Jim?"

Again, no words were necessary. My curt nod was all that was required.

"Well, good on you, Tony," exclaimed my aunt as she tried to stop herself from laughing. "I should really be telling you off, but I can't see what you did that was so wrong. This lad was going to hit you. The only reason his dad is brassed off is that you got your punches in first, and it's very embarrassing for a fourteen-year-old to be bashed up by someone who's a couple of years younger. You have nothing to be worried about, or ashamed of. I am sure Auntie Kathleen realises this, even if she didn't say so. And Uncle Jim will most certainly come round. He's just not used to such excitement. You wait until I tell your Uncle Archie. He'll be as pleased as, er... punch."

With that, we both descended into howls of laughter. Normality had returned to Brockenhurst Avenue.

When she had composed herself, Auntie Maureen emphasised she was not condoning violence in any shape or form. But her subtle East Yorkshire voice added: "Never start anything, Tony. Just bloody well make sure you are the one who finishes things off. Your mum and I were taught that at an early age. And never apologise to anyone who tries to tell you you've done the wrong thing. You haven't. If people don't want to get hurt, they shouldn't pick on you. Plain and simple."

By the time nine o'clock came around, the traumas of earlier had started to subside. Auntie Maureen had been her usual positive self from the moment I walked into her home, and her encouragement had succeeded in putting a smile back on my face.

"Do you fancy staying here and watching some telly?" she asked as the Hai Karate aftershave advert we were both watching came to a dramatic conclusion. "I think *The Professionals* is on the box in a moment, and I have got a freshly made chocolate cake in the fridge. As a treat, I'll get you a slice and we can both settle down and see what excitement awaits Bodie and Doyle this week. You never know, you might even learn how to hit someone without doing them serious damage! And don't worry, I will call Auntie Kathleen and tell her you're staying here for a bit longer."

The comment provoked yet more laughter from us both, albeit my own conscience wouldn't allow me to chuckle as fulsomely as Auntie Maureen.

Although I had only been alive for a few short years, I had been taught from an early age that a slab of cake and a good, pulse-racing TV programme had far-reaching restorative powers. And that evening, the case was proven beyond doubt. So much so, when it was time for me to return to number thirteen, two and a half hours had passed by in the blink of an eye – and my jaw ached after it had been overworked in the extreme. ✳

NINE

Spitfires and Knickerbockerglories

JESSIE ELLIS WAS AN UNASSUMING lady who you underestimated at your peril. Quiet, reserved, and with a hair-do akin to Ena Sharples (one of the most popular characters in *Coronation Street* during the sixties and seventies), she would often be heard telling amusing stories around the dinner table, found completing newspaper crosswords as often as possible with her sister, Kathleen – always with a cup of tea by her side – and, when the occasion allowed, thrashing the unsuspecting and unwary at a game of cards. Nobody could pinpoint where Auntie Jessie had honed her considerable skills and aptitude for the likes of Rummy, Newmarket and Fives, but develop them over the years, she had, until she was acknowledged by everyone as the undisputed, card-wielding powerhouse of our family. Even my mum yielded to her superiority – and for that to happen, she had to be someone who possessed special qualities.

Since I had arrived in Cottingham, I hadn't seen her anything like as much as I had wanted. Indeed, the trip to

Harrogate being the exception, I really hadn't seen much of her at all. But today, the last Wednesday of my brief fortnight would be different: Auntie Jessie would be visiting all day, and there would be ample time to enjoy her company, have a bit of fun – and listen to some of her incredible stories about bygone times.

After eating my breakfast and then getting dressed, I didn't have long to wait to be in her presence. Kathleen and Jessie were creatures of habit, and Wednesday mornings were reserved for their regular three-mile round trip to Grandways, the local supermarket, which was situated down the Lane, on the invisible boundary between Cottingham and Hull. It took a good thirty minutes to reach while walking at a brisk pace, so, an early start was always required if the intrepid siblings were to be tucking into their dinners by midday.

At nine-thirty precisely, and right on cue, there was the rustle of movement outside the front door. Sweep detected it first and fired off a howl that any self-respecting banshee would have been proud of. As his barking quietened, the brass knocker rapped out a passcode befitting of a skilled Bletchley Park telegraphist – dat-dar-da-dat-dat, dat-dat. The noise confirmed Auntie Jessie had successfully negotiated the bus trip from Goddard Avenue and had arrived at her destination in good fettle.

"Hello, love," I heard her familiar voice call out affectionately, as the pale blue door was opened and Auntie Kathleen eagerly ushered her inside. "It's a peach of a day and, by gum, we'll need to set off sharpish if we're not going to fry in the sun."

No sooner had her words faded than there was an almighty commotion. I would learn later that Geronimo, the fearsome trolley Auntie Jessie took with her almost everywhere, had been lifted into the tightly-packed hallway prematurely, jamming the two sisters together. Both were large ladies and as they tried their utmost to manoeuvre themselves away from one another, there was a howl of pain as Geronimo collided with the unprotected flesh of Auntie Kathleen's pale white legs.

"Oy, Jessie, you clumsy apeth; goodness gracious, mind what you're doing," yelped an alarmed Auntie Kathleen, as their futile attempts to avert a full-on coming together failed spectacularly. For a second, a peace of sorts descended on the front of the house, suggesting matters had been resolved. Alas, this proved not to be the case.

"Oooh, you've only gone and put a hole in my bloody tights, Jessie. I'm now going to have to change them," yelped Auntie Kathleen, her frustration clear for everyone to hear. "I can't go down the Lane with a gaping hole exposing me to the elements. What if I bump into a neighbour? I'll be the source of gossip for the rest of the week. Sister, go and make yourself a tea, and have a chat with Tony, while I go and get myself ship-shape once again. I will be with you as soon as I can."

As an unimpressed Auntie Kathleen stomped up the stairs, Jessie's flushed face peered around the door. "Is there room for one more at the table?" she quipped as if everything was normal and I couldn't have possibly heard any of the drama that had just unfolded. "Tony, I am in desperate need of a cuppa so let's be having you."

After she'd made herself comfortable, and ladled a couple of steeped spoonfuls of sugar into the cuppa I had made her – 'the finest of brews,' as my mum used to say of the Yorkshire Tea variety – great aunt and great nephew talked animatedly about anything and everything for the next five minutes, including debating one of my favourite subjects: the best place in Hull where you could buy a Knickerbockerglory? For the uninitiated, such a delight is the pinnacle of desserts, being a culinary concoction comprising vanilla ice cream, mango, raspberries, blueberries, pistachios, and anything else that catches the eye. It is usually presented in a foot-tall glass, complete with Hundreds and Thousands sprinkled on top. Throughout the glorious seventies, this represented the height of sophistication to a youth who freely laughed aloud at the impressions of Mike Yarwood and the risqué jokes of Stan Boardman.

Like her younger sibling, Auntie Jessie had the knack of knowing how to get me in a good mood, and this process invariably involved talking about puddings and dangling a huge incentive in front of my nose.

"If you are a good lad today, I'll have a word with Auntie Kathleen and see if she'll let me take you to the Wimpy restaurant in the centre of town before you go back home. I have asked around and been told it's here that you'll get the best Knickerbockerglory in Yorkshire," she declared. "Mind you, Tony, from what I hear, there's every chance I won't have to spend a single penny on you, as it seems you have got yourself into a few scrapes during the last few days. Whatever have you been up to?"

My shoulders slumped. Bad news travels quickly, and I quickly tried to find the right words to confess my all. But before I could account for my actions and misfortunes, Auntie Kathleen reappeared. Irritation continued to be written on her face, and after looking at her legs I could see why: she was now wearing a resplendent pair of bright red tights, the kind that provokes an almost physical reaction when you are forced to look at them. There was no sign whatsoever of the skin-coloured variety that had covered her legs a few moments earlier. Funnily enough, in a strange kind of way, even though they were so garish, they proved the near-perfect partner for her equally grotesque dress, that was daubed in what I later found out were supposed to be shapes that resembled tangerines.

"Come on, you two dawdlers," she boomed, her malfunctioning wardrobe one of the reasons she seemed so peeved. "There isn't time to be sitting down and having a leisurely chat. There is shopping to be done, and we haven't got all day. So, let's be having you – and you can take your eyes off my tights, Tony. These are the only pair I could find, and in times of emergency, beggars can't be choosers."

Auntie Jessie and I exchanged knowing looks, with the faintest of smiles momentarily appearing on our faces. They were soon wiped away after another sudden and scolding verbal broadside from Auntie Kathleen, who sensed she was being silently ridiculed. Her words certainly had the desired effect as we were on our feet and marching out of the house in next to no time.

"You really are the clumsiest of people, Jessie," she said brusquely as she locked the back door and yanked Sweep's lead, bringing the uncooperative mutt to heel. "That damned trolley of yours will be the death of both of us one day."

With her frustrations vented, off we scooted. Within a few seconds, we were into our stride; up the Avenue and all the way down the Lane to Grandways. For people like aunts Kathleen and Jessie, it was still a treat to go to the new generation of shops. From here, they could buy almost everything under one roof. Grandways, and Jacksons before it, were the pinnacle of the shopping experience in Cottingham and Hull, and my two aunts always looked forward to indulging themselves whenever they could. From start to finish, it lasted approximately an hour. By the time we left the supermarket, Geronimo and Auntie Kathleen's equally robust four-wheeled fortress was overflowing with tins, bottles and bags of produce. In three heavy-duty bags was the overspill – bags of sugar and rice, and enough cereal to keep everyone fed for a month, never mind a week! As a 'treat', I was given the responsibility of carrying them.

On our way back, we made two important detours. The first was to a newsagent at the Hall Road crossroads, from where Auntie Kathleen collected her copies of *The Dandy* and *The Beano*, two comics that continued to bring unbridled happiness into the lives of two aunts. She had been buying them for as long as anyone could remember, keen to discover what dastardly deeds the likes of Dennis the Menace, Bully Beef, Roger the Dodger, the Bash Street Kids and Billy Whizz had been up to. I loved them too, and pored over these national treasures from cover to cover when I had the opportunity. As I anticipated what was to come, my mind was taken off the dead weights of the three shopping bags. I was certain my arms had grown at least a couple of inches since we had left Grandways.

I found myself regularly checking the comics hadn't fallen from Auntie Kathleen's trolley, as she took us on a fast-paced march to the mobile fish van that came to this part of Cottingham and parked up near Keswick Gardens (a long avenue featuring two lines of uniform semi-detached houses). From here, Auntie Kathleen's stash of haddock fillets and roll mop herrings were purchased every week. Freshly caught, the haddock (as well as some homemade chips and mushy peas) would be the centre-piece of tonight's tea. For some unfathomable reason, or perhaps because my family liked to be different from everybody else, Wednesdays were the regular 'fish nights' at Auntie Kathleen's, and everyone looked forward to savouring her fodder. The roll mops, meanwhile, would provide tasty sustenance for whoever fancied a taste of the pickled delight when their stomachs rumbled. Such was their popularity, there were rarely any left in the pantry within twenty-four hours of them being bought.

When we got back home, we were running late. It was almost twelve-thirty – 'dinnertime' as Yorkshire folk like to call it. It took a good fifteen minutes to pack away all the food in the pantry and over-fill the other cupboards that made this particular scullery bulge with culinary delights. As I stood by the doorway to the front room, sur-veying the scene, I could see both of my aunts were thor-oughly worn out. A combination of the heat and the exer-cise had left them low on energy and in need of some much-needed kip, which would most surely follow after we all had a bite to eat.

"Can I read the comics?" I requested as my aunts started making the dinner. "I promise I will look after them and put them back on the table once I have finished." This was a vital consideration because both of my aunts had to have their weekly dose of *The Beano* and *The Dandy* imme-diately after lunch, shortly before they undertook another daily routine: their afternoon nap. And for them to do that, they needed to be close to hand.

After tucking into a tasty salad, consisting of succulent chicken breasts, cucumber, radishes, lettuce, pork pie, tomatoes and spring onions, washed down by an obligatory cup of tea, my aunts appeared to be contented. They eased themselves into the comfy chairs in the front room and quickly became absorbed in the comics. For a good thirty minutes, they digested every morsel of mirth and merriment, regularly breaking the peace of the afternoon with a sudden hoot of laughter. Then it was time for them to close their eyes.

"We're just going to have some time to ourselves now," said Auntie Kathleen. "Why don't you go into the back garden and be a good lad by cutting the lawn? Uncle Jim's lawnmower is in the shed. By the time you've finished, we'll be as good as new, and ready to take you into town for a walkabout and, if you're a good lad, that Knickerbockerglory treat you've spent all day thinking about."

Before I could respond, they had both tilted their heads onto the plump cushions behind their necks, closed their eyes and made it plain to me that they did not wish to be disturbed. There was little doubt I had been left to my own devices for the next half an hour. On recent evidence, this could have been a dangerous time for anyone in the surrounding streets. But, after the episodes of recent days, I had vowed solemnly to be a good lad, and I was determined to be true to my oath. I went to the shed – the one bought several years earlier to replace the unfortunate wooden fortress that had been devastated by Uncle Fred's firestorm – and found a rust-encrusted contraption, nominally known as a 'lawn mower'. It had clearly seen much better days and looked as if its blades would not be up to the job, as Sweep's paws (and other body parts) had turned

Auntie Kathleen's lawn into something akin to a moon landing strip. I freed it from under a pile of junk, wiping away a dense covering of cobwebs and dust as I did so. I shook my head in despair: there was no way this was going to work. But looks can be deceptive, and after spending a few moments giving it a thorough clean and testing the blades, I chanced my arm on the green patches that constituted a lawn. At first, the mower struggled. It's engine misfired and it seemed to find the terrain not to its satisfaction. But I persevered, and soon the wheels started to gain greater traction. Soon it was eating up the long grass and firing on all cylinders, bringing a degree of respectability to Auntie Kathleen's pastel green clusters. After I had completed the final cut, I stopped, wiped some beads of sweat from my brow, and admired my handiwork (as all males like to do). I decided I was happy with the fruits of my labour.

It was at that moment I heard it – a shriek full of absolute pain and anguish.

At first, I thought somebody had fallen and hurt themselves, or worse. I looked to see where the sound was coming from. But I couldn't see over the tall fences that separated the garden of one house from that of another, and because it was another warm summer's day, many windows were wide open, allowing the sounds of everyday living to prevent me from pinpointing the source of the noise. By the time I heard a fourth loud groan, I started to panic. It sounded dreadful, as if somebody was really in agony. I had no option: I had to awaken Auntie Kathleen.

"Whatever is it?" she asked groggily, as I disturbed her well-earned slumber by prodding her shoulder repeatedly. "Whatever it is, Tony, you had better have a good reason to wake me up. I'll have you know I was just having a very pleasant dream until I felt you jabbing my arm."

I immediately told her what I had heard.

"That'll be Jack, Mr Payne to you" she responded with gentleness in her voice. "He lives at number seventeen. The Japanese did for him in the war, and he has never been the same since he came home. Sadly, there's nothing anyone can do to help him. He fought with your Uncle Jim in Burma, but he was captured and forced to build a railway in terrible conditions that ruined his body, and he has never truly healed. He's now bedridden, and every day he feels the agony of the suffering and torture he experienced. All he can do is release the pain in the only way he knows how. But although you have heard his cries, be in no doubt that he is a very brave man."

Even though I had lived in the Avenue for much of my young life, and visited regularly ever since we had moved away, I had never met Mr Payne. I had heard his name mentioned on numerous occasions, as he and his wife had been neighbours seemingly forever, and I often said hello to his two daughters. But of the man himself, I knew absolutely nothing. I decided there and then that I would try to find out more, albeit I would have to bide my time, as Auntie Kathleen was eager to put a stop to the conversation.

"Those were dreadful days, Tony," she said in a near whisper. "You can't imagine what people experienced and were forced to do during those terrible times. It's not something to be talking about right now. Maybe sometime in the future. Let's get ourselves ready to go into the city. Perhaps you'd like to go and knock on Auntie Maureen's door as see if she would like to bring your cousin, Emma, out for the remainder of the afternoon?"

My disappointment at not being able to talk about Mr Payne and the war years was instantly forgotten. It was a subject that had fascinated me ever since my grandad had shown me his war medals, earned when he fought Erwin Rommel's formidable Afrika Korps. Like so many things in life, there would be an opportunity at a more convenient time. Right now, a trip into Hull, with a ride on a double-decker bus and the lure of a Knickerbockerglory, was an important matter – one that had to be pursued with the utmost vigour.

We had been sitting in the Wimpy restaurant on King Edward Street for almost an hour, and I was getting impatient. I had eaten my beef burger with gusto; even the pickled gherkin had been consumed, barely touching the sides of my mouth as it was propelled into the abyss that is my stomach. The same fate befell the portion of chips that accompanied it. This American-style fare had been captivating the good people of Hull since the sixties when the fast-food chain first opened its doors in the city. More than a decade earlier, the place had been sparkling clean; a go-to haven, with long queues of wannabe diners queuing round the clock at the weekend. Fast forward a few years and there was a faded sign hanging in the window, appealing for participants in 'the great Womble competition' – a reference to the strange, furry creatures that dominated our tellies at the time, singing a bizarre range of pop songs and starring in their own children's series on the BBC. Tired and well past its best, the restaurant seemed to be the living embodiment of the city I loved, one highlighting the extent of its current decline. But I couldn't have cared less about the state of my surroundings that particular day, although for fifteen minutes, or so, my threadbare patience was sorely tested. For what seemed like an an intolerable amount of time, I had been forced to listen to the conversation of my three aunts, who were talking about things no young male should ever have to listen to, namely the latest twists in the plots of *Coronation Street* and *Emmerdale Farm*, and hairstyles for ladies of a certain age. And when their banter started getting slightly stilted, my baby cousin piped up, her howls silencing my aunts instantly and forcing annoying infantile gushing noises out of all their mouths.

My mood improved considerably at four o'clock precisely, when I spied a waitress walking briskly. She was carrying a tray. On it was a tall Knickerbockerglory – and they both seemed to be heading in my direction. My aunts ceased their chit-chat as the waitress approached our table, and smiles broke out on their faces when she asked: "Is there someone called Tony sitting at this table?" All their eyes turned to me. My excitement knew no bounds, and I could barely speak. For a few precious moments, I forgot everything, and life went by in a blur as I tucked into the nearest thing there has ever been to culinary perfection. I was dragged out of my trance-like state only when Auntie Maureen warned: "Be careful, Tony. If you scrape the sides any harder with that spoon, you'll be eating shards of glass."

I looked at the distinctive bowl. Where a few minutes ago there was something equally as valuable as the Jules Rimet Trophy standing in front of me, there was now just an empty vessel, soiled by the occasional trace of whipped cream and strawberry sauce. My encounter with paradise was fleeting, tasty and thoroughly worthwhile. But it was now definitely over, and the experience had lasted less than one hundred and eighty seconds.

"Well, look at the time," said Auntie Jessie, winking mischievously to me with her right eye. "We need to make our way back to Cottingham. Jim, Fred and Archie will be wondering where we have got to – and they'll soon be complaining that their stomachs need filling. Afterwards, there's the small matter of a game of cards before I make my way home. So, let's be having you all. On your feet, ladies and young Master."

The journey back to number thirteen proved to be very uneventful, except for a heavily sweating man, who chose to sit next to Auntie Maureen for the duration of the journey. Bald, fat and with a swarthy complexion, his ample folds of flesh in the midriff area of his body seemed to envelop some of Auntie Maureen's smaller frame. As a result, her face had been a picture of controlled disgust. Thankfully, the discomfort she had experienced ended when our bus stop came into view and we were all able to disembark. As the double-decker rumbled down the road, pulled onwards by a diesel engine that toiled hard, she decided to share her feelings about the experience with anyone who'd listen. Her acerbic and funny comments provoked howls of laughter from my aunts, who I had heard saying on many occasions 'cleanliness is next to god-liness'. If it was, the unfortunate wretch who sat next to Auntie Mo was likely to find himself engulfed in flames as soon as he met Saint Peter at the pearly gates!

Dinner was a concoction: rollmop herring and a bit of salad for those who wanted it, there was also brussels pate and toast, which was Auntie Jessie's number one choice; and there was Uncle Jim's favourite: haddock and chips.

"You can't beat a plate of chips that have been fried in beef and pork dripping," he said, after leaning back in his chair and loosening his black leather trouser belt. "And when the fish is fresh from the docks, you will be eating a meal that's fit for a Queen. Isn't that right, Kathleen?"

Hearing her name, my aunt turned her head away from the conversation she was enjoying with her sister and looked directly at Uncle Jim. With an expression akin to a mother appraising a child that has repeatedly been asked to sit on the naughty step. "Yes, Jim," she said. "But thank goodness we don't put that statement to the test and we are able to eat different meals. For I think you would be the first to start complaining if I did serve you fish and chips every night for your tea." The comment brought a touch of rouge to the face of Uncle Jim, and his embarrassment was further heightened when he started coughing uncontrollably and had to dash to the toilet, where he eventually brought things under control.

"Men do say some daft things, don't they?" stated Auntie Jessie, seemingly forgetting I was still at the table. "They utter the first things that come into their heads, and it's usually a load of tripe. My Jack was a lovely soul, but he was also prone to saying many a daft thing. He didn't mean anything by it. I just think it was the way he was made, and every man I have ever met seems to be afflicted with the same condition. Rather than keep their mouths shut, they feel they have got to say something no matter how daft it is. They really are strange creatures."

Auntie Kathleen nodded her head in approval, while I pretended I hadn't heard a word.

With tea done and dusted, my aunts quickly embarked on

the nightly clean-up operation, which saw me employed as chief dryer-up, and Uncle Jim, who had made a full recovery from his coughing fit, tasked with cleaning the dirty dishes, cutlery and pans. It was a well-practised procedure, with everyone knowing their roles. As we worked our way through the pile of soiled earthenware, the conversation turned, for some reason, to the war years. Mr Payne was not mentioned, nor were the Podbiereskis. Instead, the talk was all about what women like Jessie and Kathleen had experienced.

"Do you remember when a Messerschmitt fighter plane flew up the Avenue firing its guns at anything that moved?" recalled Auntie Kathleen. "Hull had just been bombed by the Luftwaffe, and we could hear bombs exploding and see buildings being razed to the ground. And then this plane appeared out of nowhere and started spraying its bullets everywhere."

"Aye, it was an awful time," reflected Auntie Jessie, remembering the horrors of May 1941 (many years later, I would learn Hull was one of the most bombed cities in Britain, with ninety-five per cent of homes suffering bomb damage). "It's a good job I could get to the airbase quickly and get my own plane airborne. A few of us were able to shoot down a few German bombers and eventually forced their planes to stop attacking the city."

I looked directly at Auntie Jessie, shaking my head and not quite believing what I had just heard. It took a few seconds for me to comprehend the words that had come out of her mouth.

"W-h-h-a-a-a-t?" I stammered, struggling to contain my composure. "Did you fight in the war, Auntie Jessie?… Were you a fighter pilot?… Did you kill Germans?… I-I-I didn't know ladies were allowed to do those sort of things…"

With Auntie Kathleen smiling warmly and taking over the pot drying duties, Auntie Jessie guided me into the sitting room and sat me down on the settee. Her face was a picture of innocence. What she was to tell me, I would believe for several years.

"It's been a secret for a long time," she said in a hushed voice. "But as we're family, I can tell you, now the war has been over for a long time. The truth is, I was a pilot in a secret squadron. All of us were women. We had to be of a certain age, and of a certain height – less than five feet four inches tall. And we also had to promise to keep fighting the Germans in the air, or on the ground, because in the early years of the war there was a real possibility Britain was going to be invaded. The nazis controlled the air and the sea after they'd blitzed their way through almost all of northern Europe. Everyone thought we didn't stand a chance. Women like me were chosen because there weren't nearly enough men to do all of the jobs that needed to be done. So, I was trained in secret and then given my own Spitfire, which I flew almost every day and night between March and July."

I was mesmerised. Auntie Jessie – my flesh and blood – was a war heroine. She had fought the Germans and nobody had known about it for more than thirty years. I was one of the first to be told. I was not sure even my Mum knew about it (she had told me Auntie Jessie had worked in a munitions factory). My dear aunt was so humble and convincing, I found myself hanging on her every word, wanting to believe everything she told me.

"I must have shot down at least forty German planes," she continued. "And I was never shot down.

Neither did the planes of the other pilots I flew with. We were like an invisible squadron that caught the Germans completely by surprise. It was frightening, it was exhilarating, and in its own little way it played a very small part in Britain winning the war."

With every word, my heart was beating faster and swelling with pride. As a sapper in the Eighth Army, my grandad had been wounded on two separate occasions. Mum had told me one of these required him to have open heart surgery in the field without any anaesthetic to dilute the pain. Many wounded soldiers experienced something similar. For several years, I hadn't seen him, for he moved away from the Avenue after my grandma died. That was in 1972. But even though he was absent, to me, my grandad would always be one of my heroes. So, too, was Uncle Jim. Like Mr Payne, he had witnessed some terrible things while fighting the Japanese, as the war in Burma was fierce and uncompromising. He, too, was a man I put on a pedestal. Yet discovering my Auntie Jessie had also thwarted the Germans was as good as it got; from that day, she assumed goddess status. For another thirty minutes, she continued to tell me stories of derring-do; seemingly lost causes, and of brutal dog fights that somehow came good for Auntie Jessie and the RAF pilots she flew alongside. By the time she had finished letting me into her secret world, I was utterly exhausted.

"You can't say anything to anyone about these things," she cautioned after a fresh cup of tea had been placed by her side by Auntie Kathleen, who continued to have a 'knowing look' in her eyes. "This has to be our big secret for the time being, Tony. We don't talk about certain things for a very good reason. One day, I will be able to tell you it's okay to say something. But not right now. Until then, you must not tell anyone, not even your Mum. Do you promise me you'll do this?"

Since I started school, I had struggled to concentrate. Only Hull City, my growing interest in rugby (union and league), and a fascination with the military stimulated me enough to retain my attention, and at that precise moment I was concentrating like never before, trying to imagine what Auntie Jessie would have looked like in her pilot's uniform, and what kinds of emotion would be etched on her face when she was firing her machine gun and the bullets ripped through the fuselage of an enemy plane. Despite my urge to tell the world about my aunt's exploits, I could only do one thing, so I nodded my head. I would not betray her.

"Enough of all this talk of the war," said Auntie Kathleen, clapping her hands and signalling the time for conversation was over. She had been sitting on her comfy throne for the last few minutes, quietly listening to everything her sister had revealed. Being young and naive, I thought nothing of it, only that she must have been sworn to secrecy sometime earlier and was, therefore, able to eavesdrop on top-secret conversations like this one. "Let's get the table out and prepare for a game, or two, of cards. Maybe tonight, your aunt's luck will run out and someone else will be able to claim the bragging rights."

Almost two hours later, any thoughts the rest of us had of upstaging Auntie Jessie had been well and truly shattered. Time and again, she defeated the best efforts Uncle Jim, Auntie Kathleen and myself could muster, clucking aloud as she played her winning hands. Thankfully, she had to leave number thirteen in time to catch the nine o'clock bus, so she would be home well before dark. In the scheme of things, our suffering was relatively short, albeit you wouldn't have known it. As she glanced at her watch, and realised the time to leave was drawing near, Auntie Jessie did what she always did – pulled at the sleeves of her dress before making sure every strand of her dark, cropped hair was all in place. She then puffed out her cheeks and used all her might to push herself out of the chair from where she had crushed all our hopes once again. "Can I walk down the Lane with you?" I asked as she said her goodbyes to Auntie Kathleen and Uncle Jim, and folded her apron into a neat square, placing it carefully in Geronimo. "You can tell me more about what it was like being a fighter pilot…"

Oops. A sharp look out of the corner of her eye told me I had said too much.

"What did I tell you, Tony, about certain things that can't be talked about in the open?" said Auntie Jessie, aiming her comment directly not at me, but at Uncle Jim, whose incredulous expression I mistook for surprise. "Some of the people in this room are unaware of what I did all those years ago. Please remember what I told you? I am relying on you to keep my secret. Now, I am happy for you to keep me company to the bus stop but I'm afraid we'll have to talk about something else – and that's only if your aunt and uncle say it's alright for you to come along."

"It's fine. He can keep you company," confirmed Auntie Kathleen, doing her best to keep a straight face. "But no detours on the way back; straight back here, and no loitering anywhere after your aunt has boarded her bus. I want you in this house as quick as possible, with no excuses. You've got to keep Uncle Jim and Sweep company on their evening walk, and they'll both be waiting for you."

I threw Auntie Kathleen a smile. Then, taking Geronimo in both hands, I guided the heavy trolley out of the front door and onto the Avenue. Auntie Jessie followed in my footsteps, less than a yard behind. As we walked clear of number thirteen, she turned to me and said: "Now then, how do you fancy hearing about the night I shot down two Heinkel bombers..." ✳

TEN

Getting my collar felt

I WILL NEVER FORGET THURSDAY the twenty-fifth day of August. From the moment I awoke to the sound of Uncle Jim taking the chamber pot down the stairs at seven o'clock in the morning, to almost ten at night, when Sweep crawled back into the house after his regular evening walk, the sun's fiery red glow dominated the East Yorkshire sky-line. Like most boys of my age, I didn't really appreciate the awe and wonder of the universe and such things. But even so, on this particular day, I couldn't help being over-come by the golden orb's perfection and sheer beauty – and the endless stream of twenty-four-degree heat it emit-ted from so far away.

There were less than forty-eight hours left before my mum would make the journey from Leicestershire, and return me from whence I had come – the distant East Midlands. Whereas there had been quite a lot to look for-ward to during the last few days, today was very different. As soon as she had climbed out of bed, Auntie Kathleen's day was already defined by the need to do the weekly washing and ironing. Indeed, as she followed Uncle Jim down the stairs (and the chamber pot's contents audibly sloshed from side to side), I could hear her declaring it was "perfect washing weather". For me, such a statement was the worst possible news. Staying at home all day doing domestic chores may have been all well and good for adults, but it certainly wouldn't do for me. Playing with my Airfix soldiers had lost its appeal almost as soon as I arrived in Cottingham, and I couldn't countenance the thought of dragging Sweep out for yet another laborious walk. As it had done so spectacularly on my first day, the threat of boredom started to take a firm hold, and the more I tried to banish thoughts of liberation and inquisitiveness, the more my mind went into overdrive. In the end, I had no alternative but to give in to my urge to seek adventure.

After breakfast had come and gone, and uncles Jim and Fred had long departed on their trusty bikes to complete their waged labours, I asked Auntie Kathleen if I could go out for a walk. She turned from the mangle that was consuming all her energy, adjusted her glasses as she focused those probing pale blue eyes on me, and replied: "Tony, I am happy for you to go on a return trip to the moon today, just as long as you really promise to stay out of trouble and get back here at a reasonable time. As you can see, my day is not my own. I have got your uncles' washing to do, and a bit of my own and yours to boot. So, I know what I am going to be doing until teatime. Where are you thinking of going?"

That was a difficult question to answer truthfully as I didn't have a clue what I intended to do. But admitting as much would not be a good move. I needed to say something pretty convincing, and it needed to be said sharpish; all restless boys had to have a good reason to be allowed to roam. "I want to go fishing for Sticklebacks," I said, splurting out the first thing that came into my head. "I know the perfect place – down the snicket and close to the railway crossing. The beck – it's the ideal spot."

Auntie Kathleen knew exactly where I was talking about. There was a large area of overgrown land, belonging to the University of Hull, that started on Thwaite Street and stretched almost as far as Jesmond Road, Cornwall Street and Station Walk. It was the perfect place for children to play, albeit to enter the grounds without an invitation was technically trespassing, but as many a transgressor had learned over the years, the rules only mattered if you got caught in the act! And that was certainly not part of my plan. The snicket (sometimes they're called a 'ginnel' or 'jitty') ran at the rear of the university grounds and extended all the way to the railway line, and it was here that a small beck (stream) laced its way around the fauna and flora. I congratulated myself for thinking so clearly when I had been put on the spot. My suggestion was a good starter for ten, as there was a fishing net propped up in the backyard, next to where my uncles housed their bikes in the evening. I last used it a year ago when mum, myself and aunts Jessie and Kathleen visited Hornsea, and I had been allowed half an hour's grace to play on the beach after a long and boring visit to the town's famous pottery. I crossed my fingers as I saw the doubt etched all over Auntie Kathleen's face as she weighed up the pros and cons of letting me off the leash once again. We both knew I'd betrayed her trust more than once already, and she had every right to be understandably cautious. Eventually, after mulling over all the possible risks and potential outcomes, she nodded her head and gave me her blessing.

"Mind, you really had better be on your best behaviour," she added sternly, as the wheel of the mangle groaned its opposition when one of Uncle Jim's heavy work shirts got stuck in its rollers. "I can't be doing with anymore unpleasant surprises. Go and do some fishing, but please stay away from trouble – and make sure you release any fish you catch. Let's try and finish your holiday on a high note."

Her last comment brought back memories of my infamous attempt to raise a nest of young abandoned birds that I'd 'rescued' when I was a nature-obsessed six-year-old. I had found the four chicks in number seven's back garden. Rather than leave them in the freshly clipped Hawthorn bush, I skilfully extracted the nest and placed it in a shoe box that I took into my grandad's and grandma's wooden veranda, where I proceeded to place them on the table and sought to tend for their every need. Despite my best efforts, they survived less than twenty-four hours. It was an act on my part that my mum and family rarely let me forget. All my relatives seemed to have very long memories, and without fail, they always brought up the incident (in a variety of ways) whenever I expressed an interest in looking after small animals. Banishing this painful episode from my mind as quickly as I could, I enthusiastically agreed to every condition Auntie Kathleen imposed: I would be back well before teatime; I wouldn't deviate from the main road, or open paths, on my travels; I'd definitely return everything I caught back into the stream; and I would avoid getting into scrapes at all costs.

"You can trust me, Auntie Kathleen," I said as I ran up the stairs to change into my shorts, training shoes and trusty, sweat-stained Hull City shirt. "I will only be out for a few hours and, when I get back, I can help you make tea."

At that precise moment, I was happy, I felt free – and butter wouldn't have melted in my mouth.

By ten thirty, I was striding down the Avenue with purpose, eagerly looking forward to a few hours of liberation. In my right hand I clutched the fishing net, although I had doubts over how much use it would be, after all, it had only been an excuse to get outside. I enjoyed being by myself, doing my 'own thing'. There was potentially a lot to do and see, and not enough hours in the day to accomplish half of the things that were racing through my mind.

I had decided to take the Endyke Lane route to the stream, which meant walking past the neat rows of allotments that accommodated the green-fingered locals who loved nothing more than growing their own vegetables, fruits and flowers. It was located in a small expanse of fertile land sited between Brockenhurst and Lyndhurst avenues. For hungry youngsters like me, this was a prime spot to launch clandestine raids on the ripest crops of strawberries, raspberries, blackcurrants and gooseberries. Success or failure depended on whether an allotment holder had left their patch unattended. If they were in situ, urchins like me had no chance of filling their bellies. Today, however, I appeared to be in luck, for hardly anyone was tending their prized soils; this meant it wouldn't take long to decide which allotment would provide me with my preferred choice: big, plump gooseberries! The reason I preferred the 'goosegog', as we liked to call them, was they were far sweeter than any of their rivals if you got to them at the right time of the season (conversely, if you didn't get your timing right, the taste was incredibly bitter). August was definitely the right time of the year. So, as soon as I cleared the short, hedge-lined track that led from Auntie Kathleen's, I crouched down on the flattened mud that constituted a path and got my bearings. A cursory glance to my left and right helped me realise I needed to make a beeline for the shed at eleven o'clock, which was approximately sixty yards to my left. There I would be reunited with my favourite hunting ground.

As I started to make my way to the flourishing goose-gog bushes, I heard a shed door open and two male voices break the tranquillity of the morning peace. I strained my neck in an attempt to catch sight of where the noises were coming from. It was a plot directly to my right.

"The ground's getting bloody hard," said a tall man as he scratched his bald pate and rummaged in one of his pockets. "The sun has dried it out and it's set like concrete. I'll give it another fifteen minutes and then I'll call it quits. There's little point staying any longer. I'll finish things off with a bit of watering and then I'll make my way home."

"Me, too," responded his friend, as he swung his arm wildly in my direction, depositing what was left of his brew on a multitude of grateful vegetables. I continued to watch the two men between the stems of the tall green bean plants that hid my presence. After a few minutes, I started to get impatient: didn't these blokes know how hungry I was?

"I've got to go and buy a couple of things from Skeltons for tonight's supper, so I think I'll clock off at the same time as you," continued the second man. "Thanks for a smashing cuppa and chat. I'll catch you in the morning."

As the two men shook hands and bid their farewells, I instinctively pulled myself closer to the lush vegetation. I estimated they were less than forty feet away from where I was hiding, and I would be doomed if either looked too closely in my direction. I looked at the amber stripes of my City shirt, which wouldn't take much detecting if they happened to look where I was hiding. And then I would be in trouble. For what seemed like an age, I crouched, remaining deathly still and quiet even when my legs started to ache. Then, the man needing a curd cheesecake, or two, departed. Five minutes later, the tall chap, who bore more than a passing resemblance to the Hollywood actor, Yul Brunner, secured the padlock on his shed door, placed his obligatory flat cap on his head and walked away in the direction of Lyndhurst Gardens. In next to no time he'd completely disappeared from view. At last, I was on my own.

I looked at my Timex wristwatch (a Christmas gift from Auntie Kathleen and Uncle Jim a couple of years earlier). It was ten past eleven, which meant I had been in hiding for almost forty minutes. It was little wonder I had lost track of the time. With the coast now seemingly clear, I crawled as quickly as I could to the dense row of bushes that would soon offer up their delicious fruit. I had visited here before and, so far, this particular allotment had never disappointed. This year's crop looked like it might be the best ever. Bushes were weighed down with row after row of bulbous berries, their green skins strained to breaking point. To me, they looked to be as perfect as any fruit could be. I reached out and plucked four goosegogs from the same stem and instinctively jammed them all in my mouth. Mum had always told me I was a glutton, and I was definitely slightly over-eager on this occasion.

The taste of those gooseberries is something I will never forget. To say they were sour beyond belief is an understatement in the extreme: they were revolting and I quickly spat them out (not quite as dramatically as Uncle Jim, when he drank his sabotaged cuppa). Some of the acidic juices found their way into my air pipe, and I was forced to abandon my camouflaged hiding place and ride out a violent coughing fit. As I stood retching and cough-ing, the handful of men tending their plants on the far side of the field just continued with their toils as if nothing out of the ordinary was happening. They were either thor-oughly absorbed in their work, or the misfortune of an errant youth was of no concern to them. Thankfully, after a couple of minutes, I managed to bring the coughing under control. It was time to get away. I walked back to the hardened mud path, where I picked up the discarded fish-ing net and nonchalantly continued on my journey, look-ing forward to my next bit of adventure. Had I been more reflective and thoughtful, I might have realised this was a foretaste of what was to come…

I had only been in the company of Carl Graham and Stephen Moorcroft for an hour. During this short time we had quickly formed a bond and enjoyed our first success.

The beck I had told Auntie Kathleen about was home to a large quantity of sticklebacks and freshwater shrimps, which I started to harvest as soon as I arrived at my destination. I had known about this place for several years, ever since I had attended Cottingham's main primary school, and used the snicket to get there. Its shallow, clear water made it easy to observe both as they darted along the shallow sand and grit-encrusted bed, their silver and brown bodies creating vivid patterns as they zigzagged and outpaced the slow-running water. Nature, in its rawest and simplest form, is indeed a wonderful sight. After I had got my bearings and decided where I would position myself to gain the maximum effect, I went foraging. I needed to find a large tin can, or a glass jar, which I could use as a temporary home for whatever I caught. And it was as I explored the lush undergrowth of the University's grounds that I stumbled across Carl and Stephen.

Both boys lived close by, and like me they were bored – bored to distraction! In theory, long school holidays sound great. Six or seven weeks away from the daily grind of the classroom was surely something to celebrate and enjoy? Actually, for lads like us, it wasn't. Our reality was somewhat different, for after three and a half weeks the novelty of being out of school had well and truly worn off. Unless you had a hundred different friends, who all enjoyed doing very contrasting things, every day became monotonous. I often dreaded waking up. You were forced to see the same people, do the same things – and even have the same conversations. It's little wonder we all went a bit stir-crazy during the summer. While my walk from the allotments had increased my appetite for fishing, the boys were engaged in a far more ambitious project: they were rummaging in the grounds looking for anything that might help them build a treehouse. They told me they had already spent several days constructing a frame in a large fir tree, and they were now looking for sturdy branches to use as walling and roofing.

"It's going to be epic," said Carl, his distinct East Yorkshire voice ringing out in the undergrowth and his enthusiasm hard to contain. "You can help us, if you like? But you mustn't tell anyone about it. If you do, they'll wreck it. You've got to keep it secret. Do you promise not to say anything?"

I nodded my head, indicating I would remain tight-lipped. "I've just come to do some fishing, and to have some fun," I said. "I'm here on holiday, and I'm going home on Saturday. My auntie has let me out for the day, which means I can help you for a few hours."

Carl (tall and lanky, and a glory-hunting Leeds United supporter) and Stephen (short and stubby and a fellow Tiger) looked happy at the prospect of having a willing helper, particularly as I was soon going to be gone from these parts, thereby ensuring their secret would be safe.

"Once we've done the work on the treehouse, we're going to do some fossil hunting," added Stephen, as the three of us walked to the fir tree with several long branches tucked under our arms. "There's loads of great rocks by the railway line, and yesterday we found ammonites and trilobites there. So, we're going back today, and you can come with us. You're bound to find something worth keeping."

I had been interested in dinosaurs and rocks ever since my godmother gave me some volcanic lava she had found in Iceland. I had spent hours studying this coarse, black mass, imagining how it had come into being. Such things fascinated me. On the rare occasions I was taken to the beach, I always checked out the rocks at the foot of the cliffs. At home, my 'finds' – a couple of ammonites and several prehistoric shark's teeth – graced the window sill in my bedroom. Also on show was a stunning piece of quartz a relative had given me. I was always on the lookout to add to my modest collection.

"I'm up for that," I replied. "I love digging around in the dirt."

It was shortly after dinner time (remember, that's midday in Yorkshire) that we turned our attention to the rocks by the railway line which runs from Hull's Paragon Station, through Cottingham and onward to Scarborough. Two iron tracks cut through the village, allowing trains to stop at the station at regular intervals every hour. Their arrivals prompted a temporary closure of Thwaite Street, where the level crossing protected pedestrians and motorists alike from the diesel locomotives that thundered up and down the lines.

My first exposure to Britain's great railway network came when my grandad took me and the rest of the family on a train trip. The age of steam was coming to a close, so our journey was taken on one of the remaining 'Puffing Billies' that graced the rails until the eleventh of August 1968, when 'dieselisation' became a reality and the remainder of the nation's coal-fired engines were consigned to museums and scrap yards. So, I had fond memories of Cottingham station, the place Carl, Stephen and I were about to explore.

We had worked on the treehouse for a couple of hours and it had come on in leaps and bounds, albeit it was decidedly shaky when more than one person attempted to climb into it. Having been badly winded when I fell from a tree the previous summer, I decided to keep my feet on firm ground and ducked out of the opportunity of joining Carl and Stephen in their citadel that stood about ten feet off the ground. I was happy enough to pass the boys the assorted building materials we had scavenged, but nothing more. Like me, Carl and Stephen were not used to hard graft, and the three of us were tired of construction work after a couple of hours. We made our way to the beck, quickly finding the place I had identified as a prime fishing spot. We took turns dipping the net in the water, following the elusive Sticklebacks and shrimps as they valiantly tried to escape capture. Some were successful, some failed, quickly becoming our captives. Those we caught were hastily placed in a couple of old five-litre Dulux paint cans we had found nestling in the weeds. Once we had cleaned them and they were filled with water, there was ample space for our 'catch'. But with the church bells of St Mary's ringing in the distance, we agreed it was time to call an end to the fishing and start the main business of the day. It promised to be the perfect end to the afternoon.

"Start looking in the embankment area," Carl said to me. "We'll take a look at the rocks on the tracks, and when a train comes, we'll just get out of the way. We shouldn't go onto the rails, but that's where we found the fossils yesterday, so that's where we'll start. If anyone comes, we'll head for the snicket and hide there until they've gone. Then we'll try again."

It was a simple plan that couldn't go wrong, and for the next forty-five minutes, or so, it worked like clockwork. Its effectiveness was tested when a large freight train rumbled along the track and we all hid from view long before it passed us. Shortly afterwards a passenger train followed its larger cousin into the station. On both occasions, we saw the signals change in plenty of time and took appropriate action. There were no problems on either occasion. Alas, the hunt for the remains of trilobites and ammonites was faring less well – until Carl struck paleontologist gold.

"Hey, I think we've found a really big one. Come and take a look," he shouted gleefully. For some reason, I checked my watch: it was two-thirty. "It's stuck in a rock. I can't get it out. You won't believe how big it is."

Needing no prompting, I raced over from the embankment area I had been combing. True enough, the discovery was everything a fossil hunter could have wished for. What looked like a huge ammonite was protruding from a disproportionally large piece of granite, and although much of it remained hidden in the dusty rock, what I could see of the fossil measured at least seven or eight inches. There was possibly a lot more to be revealed as I could only partially see its distinctive, ribbed shell.

"We need to break the rock," said Carl. "If we can open it up, the whole thing should still be intact."

Our collective excitement was palpable. Even though we'd only known each other for a few fleeting moments, the three of us were experiencing a common joy. Our excitement had united us.

Carl didn't need any prompting to start hurling the rock onto the ground, but despite his best efforts it refused to yield and give up its treasure. Every time he threw it to the floor, small shards would break away, but the main rump of the granite remained, frustrating us. We took turns hurling it against rails and rock, trying to create a major fracture. But nothing we worked. Then I heard Carl suggest an extreme solution.

"Why don't we put it on one of the rails and let a train break it apart for us?" he suggested. "Nothing will be able to withstand that kind of weight."

The idea sounded like the practical solution we needed, and because we were all so engrossed we didn't think about the bigger picture. Stephen and I instantly yelled our complete approval to the plan. Almost immediately after we had agreed the next steps, the railway signal turned from red to green, indicating the next train was only a few minutes away. It was coming from Hull, which meant it would be pulling into the station first before continuing its northbound journey. Our anticipation grew; within a handful of minutes, once it had pulled out of the station, the stubborn piece of granite that had caused us so much grief would meet its match.

"We've just got to hope the train's wheels don't crush the ammonite," I said unhelpfully. "That wouldn't be what we want, would it?"

"You prat," exclaimed Stephen cheerily. "Don't you think we know that? But we've got to try it as there doesn't seem to be any other way."

As we animatedly discussed what we hoped the broken granite would reveal, Carl picked it up, straightened his crumpled jeans, and cautiously walked to the rails. He bent down and, with careful precision, placed it on one of the heavy metal strips that ran as far as the eye could see. Only when he was happy did he make his way back to our hiding place, which we had chosen because it gave us the fullest visibility of the widest section of the track. Soon we heard the train's brakes squealing as it came to a stop at the station. It was now less than a hundred and fifty yards from where we waited. We could hear doors being

slammed shut as the guard paced up and down the plat-
form ensuring everything was in order so the train could
continue its journey. As the guard's whistle blew, indicating
it was time for the locomotive to continue onwards, the
three of us leant forward into the long grasses that hid us
from view, and we quietened, anticipating the sound of the
train's wheels gripping the iron rails as it started to build
up speed. Yet rather surprisingly… nothing happened. We
waited for a minute, then another, and possibly a couple
more. We looked at each other, shaking our heads, unable
to understand why there was a delay. None the wiser, we
strained the sinews in our necks, looking to the left, in the
direction of the station, but still, we couldn't hear or see
anything. In the end, all three of us stood up and were
shocked to see the locomotive still standing on the plat-
form. Its doors were closed, and the signal continued to
state it was safe to proceed, yet the engine and its carriages
showed no interest in continuing on their journey.

And then our peace was shattered.

The sudden screech of car brakes sent a shiver down
my spine. The noise seemingly came from nowhere,
drowning out the tranquillity of the afternoon. There was
an urgency to the commotion that sent my finely tuned
early warning system into overdrive. Carl and Stephen
were equally alarmed. The noises came from the direction
of the railway station's car park, which was positioned to
our right. We were unsighted, so didn't know what had
made the noise, or why. This meant we were completely
unaware of the uniformed police officers who had come to
hunt us down. Indeed, the first we knew of their presence
was when a booming voice caught us completely off-
guard. "Lads, I am a police officer and I know you're hid-

ing in the long grass," said one of them. "If you come out without making any fuss, I am sure we can sort out the problem you have created to the benefit of everyone."

To say we were terrified is an understatement. The simple truth is, we didn't have a clue as to what was going on, or why. And, in the few seconds we had to comprehend what the policeman had said to us, we certainly didn't appreciate what we had done that warranted the long arm of the law taking an interest in us. But one thing was very obvious: we couldn't hide any longer.

Stephen was the first to rise and make himself known. He was scared stiff. So was I, and I quickly followed him in standing up. Carl rose out of the long grass last of all. I was able to make out the shapes of two panda cars – both of them Rovers – parked in the distance. Their blue lights were flashing vigorously. Considerably closer were four uniformed officers, positioned to cut off any possible escape. All of them were well over six feet tall and looked like proverbial outhouses. One was a sergeant, and he appeared to be the man in control. "Get over here," he said, beckoning the three of us to come forward. "You silly boys have caused quite a commotion and delayed the train to Bridlington. You've got a bit of explaining to do, haven't you? So, let's be having you because every minute we're standing here means those passengers on the train will have less time on the beach; and quite rightly, they'll be blaming you for that."

As the enormity of the situation suddenly dawned on us, Carl whispered: "I think we're really in the S-H-ONE-T." I agreed, as did Stephen. We were not hardened lawbreakers, and we certainly hadn't meant to put anyone in danger, so we did as we were told. Within five minutes we were standing by the stationary pale blue and white cars, doing our best to explain what we had been up to. Thankfully, once they had regained a modicum of composure, Carl and Stephen admitted it was their idea to put the rock on the track. Much to my relief.

"What were you thinking, you daft young pups?" said the sergeant after listening to the confessions and mulling things over. "Are you really that clueless? What the three of you have done is put a train, and its passengers, at serious risk. Thank goodness the signalman spotted one of you placing the rock on the track. If he hadn't, who knows what might have happened. You might have been facing murder charges."

We hung our heads in shame, and for the first time I realised I could be in serious trouble.

In the end, the eight minutes past two service was delayed by more than forty-five minutes, as were all other services travelling towards Beverley (and beyond). It turned out that sorting matters out involved a lot more than simply removing the sixty-six million-year-old ammonite from the tracks. Safety checks needed to be completed, conversations had to take place, and everyone had to be satisfied all was in order before the train was allowed to proceed. It passed the two police cars just as we were asked to sit in the back seats, and as its wheels chimed out the rhythmic 'thud-thud, thud-thud' on the rails, we felt we were under the critical gaze and judgment of single every passenger whose journey to the seaside had been delayed by our foolishness. "Take a long, hard look at those unhappy people lads," said one of the officers. "If looks could kill, you would now be taking your last breaths."

One small factor in our favour was the recovery by

the police of the granite. Upon inspection, it was plain for all to see that there was indeed a large fossil embedded in the rock. Without ceremony, the sergeant passed it to one of his fellow sleuths, who put it in a Grandways carrier bag and placed it in the boot of one of the cars. "Make sure you look after that, Constable," he said, looking menacingly in my direction. "That rock is critical to our case against these young reprobates."

I travelled into the centre of the village in the second of the two cars, separated from my fellow accomplices. Two officers kept me company as we made the short trip to Cottingham's Victorian-era police station, which was located on Finkle Street. Both gave me the silent treatment and such was their attitude you could be forgiven for thinking they'd captured great train robber, Ronnie Biggs, not a minor feral tearaway! Thankfully, it took less than five minutes to get to our destination. Once inside the station, the three of us were spoken to individually by the sternest looking coppers I have ever seen, the type whose good looks alone could quite easily curdle milk! My interrogator asked me to give him my full name, Auntie Kathleen's and Uncle Jim's name and address (and their telephone number), a brief explanation of what had happened, and state whose idea it was to put the fossil on the tracks in the first place. I knew everything I said needed to be spot on, so I did precisely what my mum had always told me to do when I found myself in a spot of bother: I told the whole truth.

My interrogation took place in a sterile room that was intimidating. I imagined the sort of criminals who had been forced to experience exactly what I was being put through: killers, fraudsters, bank robbers – and wretches like me. Sometimes I could think too much and I started to feel overwhelmed. When I composed myself, I heard a voice ask me to sit down at a big table in the centre of the room. It belonged to a different officer who must have entered the room without me realising. I had been so absorbed by the predicament I faced that I had drifted off into my own little world.

"It beggars belief, Tony," said my inquisitor, after I had repeated everything that had happened for a second time. "I don't know whether to laugh or cry. What I don't understand is how none of you could understand the danger you were putting all those people in? Be in no doubt, you did something really dangerous today, and there are consequences for doing such things."

He fell silent for a couple of minutes, looking down at the notes he had recorded in his notebook. Sporadically, his pencil weaved from side to side. And then, all of a sudden, he was done. "That's it; all over," he barked without seeming to move his lips. "Your aunt is on her way and will be here soon. Until the sergeant has decided what is going to be done with the three of you, you're going to be put in a cell. In there, you'll have ample time to think about your reckless actions."

I heard Auntie Kathleen's voice long before I actually saw her. My incarceration had seemed to last for an eternity, but in reality, it had been in the cell for a little over an hour. As it approached a quarter to four in the afternoon, I suddenly recognised her among the general chatter taking place in the long hallway. It was like hearing the voice of an angel. "Thank you, officer, you are very kind," I heard her say from somewhere beyond the cell door. "I can assure you nothing like this will ever happen again. His uncle, and I, will be reading the riot act to him once he gets home, and his mum will also have something to say." Seconds later, the key was pushed into the door's heavy lock and a harsh metallic click confirmed the mechanism had opened. As the door swung open, the figure of Auntie Kathleen emerged. She was dabbing her eyes with a handkerchief.

"Here he is," barked the constable who had quizzed me earlier. He waved his hands and beckoned me to leave. "Someone is looking after you today, young man," he added as I walked past him. "My sergeant has said you can go back home with your aunt, but he has warned that if you step out of line again when you're in these parts you'll find yourself in serious trouble. So, please don't waste this opportunity, Tony."

Although the experience had left me slightly light-headed, I understood fully what was being offered. With the warning ringing in my ears, Auntie Kathleen took a firm grip of my arm and led me out of Cottingham police station as quickly as her legs would allow. She didn't say a word as we walked briskly to the centre of the village, where she hailed a taxi that took us all the way back to number thirteen. Silence ensued for the whole journey, and when the driver stated the cost of the fare, she simply paid him his dues, did an about-turn, and walked directly to the house.

When she next spoke, Auntie Kathleen was unambiguous and to the point: "Why do you keep letting yourself down, Tony; why do you seem determined to cause Uncle Jim and myself all this unnecessary upset and misery?" she asked in a hushed voice from her perch on the front room's throne chair. "Do you like being the centre of attention for all the wrong reasons? Can't you just enjoy coming here and visiting us? Do we make your stay so bad and so dull, that you feel you have to get yourself into trouble every time you leave the house?"

I felt wretched and was unable to offer her any kind of real explanation. At that precise moment, I could do nothing to change anything, particularly Auntie Kathleen's anger and sorrow. Never before had I seen her like this and, at that moment, I feared she would never forgive me. ✳

ELEVEN

From zero to hero in less than a day

I AWOKE ON FRIDAY MORNING having endured an evening of broken sleep and awful dreams, the type that led me to believe I was being enveloped by a supernatural force that had pulled me into a dark, unyielding abyss. I tried to banish such thoughts from my head, but no matter how many times I tried, I kept on having the same recurring visions. And because of this I hardly slept a wink.

Joy had been in short supply at number thirteen after we had returned the previous evening. At teatime – once the washing up had been completed – Auntie Kathleen announced she would be going to bed as she had a pounding headache (no doubt caused by yours truly). For the rest of the night, I was left downstairs with Uncle Jim, who didn't mention anything to me about my antics. I expected to be subjected to a shortened version of the Spanish Inquisition, yet all my uncle did was attempt to crack the *Daily Mirror* crossword and then, when he had failed miserably, watch his favourite telly programmes. By the time the BBC nine o'clock news came on the box, Sweep was wagging his tail ready for his evening walk, and still, Uncle Jim hadn't talked to me about my brush with the law. The only thing he had asked was whether I'd like to accompany him on his evening stroll with Sweep. It was almost as though Auntie Kathleen hadn't said anything. As conflicting emotions gripped me about whether I should brooch the subject with him, or not, I politely declined the offer of the walk. And as I did so, a vile smell – the type only an animal can inflict on human beings – wafted over and invaded my sensitive nostrils, and I knew the source. Earlier in the day, Sweep must have eaten something that badly disagreed with his stomach because he had unashamedly been firing off foul emissions from his nether region all evening. I had chosen to ignore them, breathing through my mouth while I gave the unpleasant aromas ample time to disperse. But this latest offering suggested the poor mutt's bowels had been contaminated by the devil himself. At a quarter past nine, as Uncle Jim and Sweep made for the back door, I decided it was time to retreat to my bedroom and consign the deeds of the day to the past. Within a handful of minutes, my sheets and blanket were pulled up to my chin, and the last of the sun's rays started to fade into the onrushing darkness. And then my troubled sleep claimed me.

The following morning saw the return of Auntie Kathleen's renowned zest for life, albeit she gave me short shrift when I walked into the scullery to have breakfast. "Is there anything you wish to say to me?" she enquired, after locking her eyes on me as I walked to the table and put two Shredded Wheat into a bowl, smothering them in sugar and cold Gold Top milk. "At your convenience, an explanation would be appreciated."

"I'm really sorry," I said. "We weren't trying to hurt

anyone. We just couldn't think of any other way to get to the ammonite. And it wasn't even my idea. One of the other lads came up with it, and he placed the rock on the rails. I didn't do anything wrong."

"Mmm. What you did wrong was to be born so bloody daft," continued my unimpressed aunt. "You were just thinking of yourselves, weren't you? There was no consideration of others. If there had been, you'd have realised that putting a great boulder on a railway line could have led to a lot of trouble. Nobody, not even three dopey lads, could surely think doing such a thing would be a sensible thing? Thankfully, the police believed you weren't trying to derail the train. And the railway company were also forgiving. But if you were a little bit older and you'd pulled the same kind of stunt, they'd have thrown the book at you; you'd have to go to court, and you could end up with a criminal record. How would I have ever explained that to your mum? I promised her I would look after you. Getting into trouble with the police is hardly looking after you, is it?"

I tried to return Auntie Kathleen's gaze, but I knew everything she had said was right. So, I just got up, walked to where she stood, and threw my arms around her waist. I had never been the most tactile of lads, but at that moment, hugging her was the most natural thing to do.

"Hey, hey, what's all this about?" she said after a couple of minutes, her coldness thawing instantly. "I know you're not a bad lad, Tony. You just seem to get into more than your fair share of scrapes. Hopefully, you'll have learned a few lessons this fortnight, and you'll start to put them into practice pretty sharpish when you get home. You're growing up, and life gets harder the older you are, particularly if you don't obey the rules."

I rubbed my eyes. Tears had formed and I was embarrassed. Auntie Kathleen sensed my heightened state of emotion. "I need some tobacco," she stated. "Will you go to Elliotts and get me a packet of Old Holborn?"

Ever since I could remember, I had hated smoking. I don't know why, for almost all of my relatives were smokers. But despite my prejudices, I'd do anything for my kind and caring aunt. I quickly ate my breakfast, got dressed, cleaned my teeth, and was on my way to the newsagents. As I approached the hedged garden belonging to the old lady, which I had used in my failed lemonade bottle heist, I glanced to my right, recalling the excitement the Sidebottom brothers, Shaun Goadby and myself felt as we were about to raid the stockpile of empty bottles located in the popular newsagent's back yard. I laughed aloud, remembering how our hope and enthusiasm turned to absolute despair as we were caught red-handed by Mr Elliott. It was then I suddenly noticed something on the path that was partly concealed by a low-lying branch. I stopped and reached for what appeared to be a strap. As I gently pulled it, I quickly discovered it was a handbag, and it certainly didn't look as though it had been thrown away. A quick glance inside revealed a purse filled with money – quite a few pound notes and at least one crisp fiver – and there was also an identity card. I checked it; the owner was a student at the University of Hull.

"Whatever have you got there?" asked Mrs Elliott, as I entered her shop. The tone of her voice alerted Gordon, her husband, who quickly appeared from nowhere. "That looks remarkably like a lady's handbag, Tony. Whatever are you doing with it?" After explaining how I had come by the bag, the Elliotts and I spent the next few minutes examining its contents. We found the purse contained more than sixteen pounds, which was a considerable sum, and there were three precious necklaces hidden in a side pocket. One of them looked quite valuable. There was also a cheque-book – and a student identity card.

"You'd think she'd have noticed she'd lost her hand-bag by now," said Mr Elliott, who stood to the side of his wife, towering over her. "If you'd have lost all these things, particularly all this cash, you'd be in a right state, Nora. I suppose we've got to decide what we're going to do with it; do we try and track her down ourselves, or do we just hand the bag over to the police and let them find her?"

"George, we certainly have not got the time to try and find this young lady," chipped in Mrs Elliott. "Let's call the police, tell them what Tony has found, and let them repatriate the bag with its rightful owner. That is the only way we can proceed. And Tony, you really have done the right thing, here. None of us know Sarah. But I can tell you this, she will be delighted to get her handbag back; and when that happens, it will be all down to your honesty."

Mrs Elliott's words brought me back to reality, as my lack of sleep caught up with me. I thanked the Elliotts for their help while remembering to ask them for a packet of Old Holborn (which strictly speaking, I shouldn't have been doing). As I started to walk out of the shop, Mr Elliott called after me. "Here, take this Tony. It's hot out there." I turned around to find a Cornetto ice cream winging its way through the air in my direction. Effortlessly, I caught it and licked my lips. "Enjoy it," he added. "You've certainly earned your reward."

By the time I returned to number thirteen, Auntie Kathleen was in the sitting room, finishing off a telephone call. Much to my relief, she looked relaxed and happy. I showed her the tobacco packet, and she indicated I should put it on the scullery table. As I did so, I glanced at the clock: my round trip to the Elliotts had taken almost forty minutes.

"You took your time," said Auntie Kathleen, once she had hung up the phone. "That was your mum. She's taken the day off and decided to come up a day early. She's looking forward to seeing all of us, but most of all, she's really looking forward to seeing you. She says she's missed you. All being well, she'll be with us for about three o'clock this afternoon."

The news caught me completely by surprise. I wasn't expecting mum to arrive a day early, and the news brought a sense of dread. Sensing my discomfort and clash of feelings, my aunt sought to reassure me.

"Don't worry. I did not say anything about what happened yesterday, and I have no intention of doing so. At long last, I hope you've learned a valuable lesson, so there's no need to ruin your mum's day, is there? And I haven't told Uncle Jim either, so you don't have to worry about him. You and I can keep it our little secret – just as long as you don't do anything so stupid again. I want us to have a nice time together, ending your holiday as all holidays should end – with plenty of laughter. It's just a shame your Auntie Jessie can't be with us."

Auntie Jessie had gone away for a couple of days with another relative, Auntie Renee. Right now, they should be strolling along the promenade at Scarborough, taking in the views of England's oldest holiday destination.

"At least someone else will win if we play cards," I said. A throaty chuckle escaped from Auntie Kathleen's mouth, followed by some heartfelt chuckles. She leant forward and ruffled my thick mop of dark brown hair. "That's more like it," she said. "Let's make sure we enjoy ourselves today."

Mum arrived shortly after three o'clock in the afternoon. I had been waiting for her, looking out of the front room window, when her distinctive Renault 4 pulled into a space on the Avenue that had been vacated by Uncle Archie less than ten minutes earlier. Parked between a Ford Zephyr and a Humber Super Snipe, her tiny French car looked quite fragile and insignificant in comparison, not that mum cared one iota. A car was a 'piece of gradually rusting metal, to be looked after, nothing more', she quipped on many occasions. Even so, I often thought it would be nice to have something with a bit more street cred than a shoebox on wheels.

Auntie Maureen was the first to greet her. She had also seen her older sister arrive, and she was waiting at the gate of number sixteen to embrace her. After a warm exchange of pleasantries, the siblings went in opposite directions, with mum heading directly for Auntie Kathleen's after she had extracted a small overnight bag from the back seat of the car. The next few minutes were a bit of a whirlwind as mum was greeted by myself, Auntie Kathleen and Sweep, with the dog barking wildly and leaping up at the stranger in his midst. He was banished to his blanket under the table and ordered to stay in his 'bed' indefinitely. With mum looking better than I had seen her in months, Auntie Kathleen asked me to go and put the kettle on. "We could both do with a coffee," she suggested, "and you can get yourself a cup of tea while you're at it. While you're doing that, your mum and I can catch up on a few things. So please close the scullery door, there's a good lad."

In the end, it took ten minutes to get everything sorted, by which time the two ladies in the front room appeared to have exchanged all their essential bits of news.

"Why don't you come and tell me about all the things you've been up to while you've been here," said mum, indicating with her hands that she wanted me to sit next to her on the settee. "Auntie Kathleen tells me you have been to the football, and had trips to Hull and Harrogate. So, what have you enjoyed the most?"

I had just started to tell mum about the warplanes that had attempted to identify us on the Yorkshire Moors, when Auntie Kathleen suddenly rose from her chair, and exclaimed: "Whatever now… what could they possibly want?"

"What's wrong?" asked my mum. Deep lines had formed on her forehead. She looked concerned.

"A police car has just pulled up outside the house, and a constable is making his way here," responded my aunt. "He doesn't look like he's very happy." As she made this last comment, Auntie Kathleen's brow furrowed and she fired off a worried look in my general direction. As the officer rapped on the front door, my heart started beating wildly. I racked my brain. Apart from yesterday, what else had I done wrong?

"Mrs Burgess?" enquired the officer politely when the door was opened. Auntie Kathleen confirmed her identity, so he continued. "Can I come in? I would like to talk to you about a matter that concerns your nephew, Tony."

"Whatever have you gone and done?" whispered mum. The stress was easy to detect in her voice. I suspected Auntie Kathleen had already told her about yesterday's excitement. But I didn't have time to respond. Within seconds, the policemen put all three of us out of our misery.

"I've got a letter for you, Tony," said the constable. "It's from a young lady who is very grateful to you. Her name is Sarah. Does that ring any bells?" A big smile took hold of my mouth, but I found myself unable to say anything. I was still stunned.

"What's this all about, officer?" asked my mum. "Who is Sarah, and why on earth is she thanking Tony?"

Both women looked expectantly at the policeman.

"While Tony reads the letter, I will happily explain everything," said the officer. Pointing to the chair normally occupied by Uncle Jim, he added; "Do you mind if I sit down? It will take a few minutes to go through everything. But don't be concerned, Tony has done something really good."

I lost count of the amount of cooing noises that came from Auntie Kathleen and how many times my mum said "gosh" when the officer explained what had happened earlier in the day. As he spoke, I couldn't take my eyes off Sarah's kind words. Her letter read:

Dear Tony,

Thank you so much for ensuring my handbag was returned safely to me. I lost it when I went to a university lecture this morning. I knew I had dropped it on Inglemire Lane, but it's such a long stretch of road, I didn't know where to start looking for it. I was devastated when I realised it was lost. I had put three necklaces

that belonged to my late Grandma into the handbag,
and I thought they were lost forever. They mean so
much to me because they are all I have to remind me
of a lady I loved dearly.
Your honesty and prompt action has ensured I am
reunited with them. And for that, I thank you from the
bottom of my heart.
Big hugs and heartfelt thanks, Sarah.

The letter was signed and dated, giving a university accommodation address on Thwaite Street, where Sarah resided during term time. By the time I had read her words a fourth time, the constable was ready to leave. He thanked my mum and Auntie Kathleen for their time and, turning to me, extended his hand. "Thank you," he said. As his giant paw gently crushed my fingers, I winced and remembered how Mr Joe had done something similar only a few days earlier. "Keep doing good things." And then he was gone, leaving the three of us to reflect.

Auntie Kathleen was the first to break the silence. "Why didn't you say anything about this earlier?" she inquired. "You've just done something really good today and not mentioned a word of it. Why ever not?"

I simply shrugged my shoulders. "It didn't seem that big a deal," I said. "I just picked the bag up and took it to Mr and Mrs Elliott. They were the ones who called the police, not me. They're the ones who should really be thanked."

Mum and Auntie Kathleen glanced at one another and smiled. As they did, Auntie Kathleen became distracted by something that was happening outside.

"Well, would you believe it?" she said, failing to contain her laughter. "Archie's just pulled up in his car, and is now getting upset because someone has pinched his space. He's yelling blue murder and pointing at a Renault 4. I wonder who the culprit might be?"

Auntie Kathleen and Uncle Jim always brought the best out of my mum. She seemed at peace when in their company. Life was much less of a struggle, and she laughed so much more when she was around people she had trusted and loved all her days. Since I had been born, her life hadn't always gone according to plan, so it was great to see her looking and sounding carefree, with any worries she may have been harbouring parked for the next few hours.

It was teatime and Uncle Archie and Auntie Maureen were sitting at the big table, having been invited to eat with us. They had brought baby Emma with them, so my mum could spend some time with her, even though she was sound asleep in her carry cot. Wary of having the full house, Sweep had crawled to a safer, less exposed spot in the scullery without making any fuss, and Uncle Archie had also forgiven mum for cynically stealing his car parking spot, such was the feel-good factor that washed over us all that day. Homemade fish and chips, with the obligatory thick mushy peas, were the icing on the cake (so to speak). Thankfully, Auntie Maureen had her own haddock fillets, bought from the same fish van that supplied the residents of Keswick Gardens. These had been added to those bought by Auntie Kathleen, to ensure all stomachs were contented. Then, as the hands of the sitting room clock continued their march towards seven o'clock, Uncle Jim reached for the pack of cards.

It was time to do battle.

"You're a lucky so-and-so," yelled a frustrated Auntie Maureen, as mum won her third game of Fives on the trot. "Come back Auntie Jessie. All is forgiven! My sister has got the luck of the devil." Mum was in her element; she loved beating the rest of us at cards. It didn't happen very often, but Auntie Jessie's enforced absence played very much to her advantage

"I'll have you know there's no luck involved," she retorted. "It's all about skill and timing. And remember, I have learned from the very best, as have you." The comment drew a knowing laugh from everyone, including Auntie Maureen.

An hour and a half later, only one face was lit up. The rest of us were defeated also-rans who had been put in our places.

"What's up with you all?" joked mum. "Why is everyone so glum? It's only a game."

"That's fine for you to say," retorted Auntie Kathleen. "You haven't just spent the last two hours losing every hand you've played. Can't we try something else, like Scrabble? At least then, we might have more of a chance."

A ripple of enthusiasm greeted the suggestion, so the cards were quickly packed away and the Scrabble board took centre stage on the front room table. Uncle Archie paired up with Auntie Maureen, while Uncle Jim and Auntie Kathleen formed their own team. Mum and I decided to play as individuals, with mum given the additional responsibility of recording the scores, while I was handed a copy of the Oxford English dictionary and elevated to the role of referee, with the power to deliver a ruling in the event of a disputed spelling. With everything agreed, and seven tiles placed in all four holders, Auntie

Maureen and Uncle Archie started proceedings. And rather predictably, it didn't take long for rancour to surface.

"That is not the way you spell 'acquire'," barked Auntie Kathleen authoritatively. "There's a 'C' before the 'Q', making it a seven-letter word."

Auntie Maureen, who had laid the tiles incorrectly, looked doubtful, but then mum entered the fray. "I can assure you it's a common mistake," she said. "Most people don't know how to spell it." The comment drew a dark look from my mum's younger sibling and she visibly bit on her tongue. And so it continued.

For the next hour, words such as 'calendar', 'apparent', 'liaison' and 'referred' were all the source of dispute and my services were called upon. I managed to negotiate these potential minefields without any blood being spilt, but then came disagreement over the word 'fulfill'. My mum was adamant the correct spelling was F-U-L-F-I-L-L. And it is – in places like the US and Australia. In England, however, there is only one 'L' at the end of the word, and we were playing the game using British-English words, which had been agreed upon at the outset by everyone, including my mother. After a torturous fifteen-minute delay to seek clarification from several learned sources, including an unproductive phone call to friends Jill and Roger Tracy, who lived in the Midlands, the decision was made to call an end to proceedings. Mum had reluctantly conceded defeat in her quest to overturn the decision, but the whole process had taken far too long. It was agreed the honours would be shared, regardless of the actual scores at the time the white flag was raised.

"Thank goodness that's over," said Uncle Archie as everything started to be cleared away. "I was losing the will to live. I can't believe we have spent the last hour arguing over how we spell a handful of words."

"I buggering well can," chimed Uncle Jim. "It happens every time we play that damned game. You just want to thank your lucky stars Jessie wasn't here. My goodness, there would have been blood on the carpet if she had been. Now, I think it's time for me to take Sweep out for his evening ablutions. So, I will love you and leave you, and hope a peace, of sorts, breaks out before I get back." Addressing Auntie Maureen, Uncle Archie and the still-sleeping baby Emma, he added: "I suspect you may be gone by the time I return, but I'm sure I'll see all three of you over the weekend, for a cup of tea, if nothing else. Sleep well. I hope the little one is out for the count for the rest of the night."

Shortly after ten o'clock, as the four of us settled down to enjoy a bedtime cuppa (and a couple of slices of Auntie Kathleen's best doorstep toast), I took a good look at my surroundings. Joey, the Budgie, was still and silent, fast asleep on his roost. He hadn't made any kind of commotion since last week when Uncle Jim had his minor meltdown. He looked extremely happy to be in the cage that had been his home for the last nine years. Sweep, meanwhile, had made himself comfortable under the table, and appeared to be dreaming, as his legs spasmed while his mouth opened and closed in a bizarrely coordinated kind of way. What a daft mutt, I thought to myself. And then my tired eyes fell on my mum, aunt and uncle, who were merrily reminiscing about growing up in East Yorkshire and remembering long-gone family members like my great-grandfather and grandmother. It was great to listen to their tales of yesteryear, of characters and personalities I never knew, but who are an integral part of my DNA.

"Our family has its roots in Hull and these parts. We are as 'Yorkshire' as you get," said my mum proudly. "It's wonderful to know the Longbone name originates from around here and can only really be found in Hull. While we don't know anywhere near them all, we can be pretty sure we are linked by blood to everyone who carries that surname. It's hard to get your head around, but it's a fact."

My ears pricked up at the statement. "Surely that can't really be true, mum?"

The look my comment generated suggested I had said far too much. "It certainly is," she chided. "Your grandad comes from a large family, and so, too, did his father. And so forth. So, it didn't take a lot for the Longbones to have such a big presence in Hull and the surrounding areas. Just look in the telephone book and you'll see for yourself. And it's exactly the same on the Foster side."

Needing little prompting, I reached for the telephone directory and thumbed through the pages until I found all the entries listed under 'Longbone'. True enough, there was column after column of them. Watching on as my curiosity grew, mum added: "One of those people is the chief fire officer of East Yorkshire. He is a first cousin of your grandad." Talk of my grandad brought back some fond memories. I wanted to ask so much more, but the hour was getting late, and we had the small matter of returning to Leicestershire in a few, short hours.

"Come on, young man. It's way past your bedtime," she declared. "You've had a good day and you need your sleep. We've got a three-hour car journey ahead of us tomorrow. So, say good night to your aunt and uncle and be off to your bed." It was useless protesting. Reluctantly, I did as I was told, and shortly after my head had touched the pillow I was fast asleep.

As I have got older (but not necessarily wiser), I have often wondered why saying goodbye can be such an awkward business? We spend days in the company of friends and family, often staying up until the early hours for days and nights on end, talking about all sorts of nonsense. Yet, when it's time to pack our bags, return home and leave some of the people we care about the most, many of us are lost for words, seemingly desperate to flee from one another as quickly as possible.

That's how it was on Saturday the twenty-seventh day of August.

Mum and I were both awake well before eight o'clock and downstairs breakfasting when Auntie Kathleen emerged from the bathroom. She had been dressing and pumping vital insulin into her body that kept her alive. Its smell, which was a bit like that emitted by a bottle of cheap nail polish remover, was overpowering and polluted the air in the front room and scullery. Yet, it was an odour we had all become so used to in recent years, for Auntie Kathleen's thrice-daily injections were an essential part of her daily routine.

"It looks like you are going to have good weather for your journey home," said my aunt, looking out of the scullery window at the clear blue sky and bright rays of late summer sunshine. "Best not leave it too long before you leave. You don't want to get caught up in Bank Holiday traffic going down the A1. That would be a nightmare."

I looked at my mum, silently hoping she would have a change of heart and delay our departure for at least another day. But it wasn't to be. My mood was not at its best, and that meant I was distracted and disinterested in just about everything. Even Hull City's away match at Crystal Palace later in the afternoon failed to spark me into life. To be honest, at that moment I couldn't care whether they lost the game or won it. Football wasn't my number one priority.

"Aye," said mum. "The traffic can be murder and it was a bad enough journey coming up here. We'll just finish our cereal and then pack our bags. Then we'll get out of your hair and let you get on with the rest of the day. Are you planning to do anything nice?"

Auntie Kathleen chuckled for the first time that day. "You know us, Ann," she said. "When do we ever do anything nice? No, Jim and I will settle down this afternoon and do our crosswords, and no doubt the horse racing will be on the box. Later, there's every chance we'll have a cuppa, or two, with Maureen and Archie, and that'll be lovely. We always enjoy their company. What about you, is there much left to do at home before you go back to work?"

While I had been in Cottingham, Mum had also taken some time off from her job at the Inland Revenue, where she was a tax officer. She had sought respite every year I visited Cottingham so she could 'recharge her batteries' which I knew were drained by being a single, working mother. "No, all is in order," she replied. "Or at least I think it is. Life seems to be settling down now there is just Tony and myself to think about. And that's good enough for me after the last few months, after the divorce got all sorted."

Mention of her failed marriage resulted in mum's

eyes moistening, and she quickly found a tissue and wiped away the tears. It was one of the rare occasions I ever saw emotion get the better of her. When she was more composed, she continued: "There's the new school term to start thinking about, so I have taken Tuesday off, and we'll be going out to get some new shoes and uniform for Tony. He's outgrown everything in the space of a few short weeks. What fitted at the beginning of June, is now three inches too short."

"I know exactly what you mean, he's really shot up, hasn't he?" observed my aunt, who talked about me as if I wasn't in the same room. "Twelve years old and almost six-feet tall. It's not natural." Then, speaking to me, she added: "You need to start putting the brakes on, Tony. You're going to cost your poor mum a fortune on clothes, and they'll only last a handful of weeks."

The two women gave each other a knowing look, the type mothers give to someone who has been through the very same shared experience of childbirth and raising a child. They smiled and mum got up from the table, squeezed my shoulders as I finished off my cereal, and gently ushered me upstairs. "C'mon, you and I have got some packing to do. And before you ask, the answer is no, you are not wearing your disgusting Hull City shirt all the way home. It's filthy and smells of sweat. It can go in with the rest of the washing. You can wear a nice clean t-shirt instead. Now, let's be having you."

It took next to no time to round up all my clothes and belongings in my suitcase, and even less so for mum, who had barely brought anything with her for the short stay. I had packed my toy soldiers away several days earlier after I had become utterly bored with them in the preceding days. So, a little over an hour after we had awoken, the two of us were set fair, ready to leave. The last two weeks had gone by so quickly; all the laughter and misdeeds were a bit blurred as I stared out of the front room window at every-day life on the Avenue. Things seemed a bit unreal until I saw Uncle Jim (still wearing his striped pyjamas) standing next to mum, with Uncle Fred putting in an unexpected appearance as well; then I knew our time was almost up. And so did everyone else.

An awkward silence prevailed momentarily and was quickly brushed aside by Auntie Kathleen, as she stepped forward, opened her arms and gave mum a crushing embrace. "Take good care of yourself," she urged of her niece. "And remember, your Uncle Jim and I are always here for you both." Mum nodded her head, whispering something I couldn't quite hear. It mattered little, for she clearly understood and appreciated the significance of her aunt's words.

"As for you, Tony, we have thoroughly enjoyed having you and you know you can come here any time. We love to see you, and I hope you feel the same way about your dear old aunt and uncles? Now, go home and make sure you do all you can to look after your mum."

I didn't know what to say as my head was filled with so many contrasting thoughts. In many ways, it had been a wonderful holiday and in other regards, it had seen me behave in a way that would be talked about for years to come – not for the right reasons! Either way, none of that really mattered at that moment. Instinctively I launched myself at Auntie Kathleen and gave her the kind of hug reserved for the most special of people. I closed my eyes, only to suddenly feel Uncle Jim's coarse hands ruffling my coiffured hair. "We always love having you come to visit," he said, giving me a wink from the corner of his left eye that only I could see. It was coded man-speak for 'I forgive you, even though you have been a right little bugger'! And he was right, I had been.

As I walked out of the turquoise front door for the last time that summer, it was already a sweltering twenty-two degrees. Some sixth sense had alerted Auntie Maureen about our departure and she was waiting for us outside, while Uncle Archie, holding my baby cousin in his arms, looked on from an upstairs window of number sixteen. He saluted in the way many an ex-Navy man does while Auntie Maureen embraced us both in turn and continued to hold her doorstep vigil as mum fired up the engine of her Renault 4, swung out of Uncle Archie's prized parking spot, and started the farewell crawl down the Avenue.

Leaving the people you love is always a sad occasion, and I tried my best to show how much they meant to me by furiously waving out of the back window. I continued to do so until my arms ached and my aunts and uncles had long disappeared from view. Then, as row upon row of tightly-packed houses passed us by, I settled down on the long leather seat and started to scan a copy of *The Dandy* I had smuggled out of number thirteen, just as mum found her most prized Elvis recording and popped it into the car's reliable cassette player. As the first bars of *Always on my Mind* drowned out the noise of the engine, and I became absorbed in the latest adventures of Lord Snooty and Korky the Cat, I suddenly felt reinvigorated and alive.

I was ready to go home. ✳

TWELVE

A birthday I'll never forget

THE PHONE RANG SHORTLY BEFORE five o'clock in the evening. It was 1979 and the thirtieth day of July had been an occasion to celebrate. It was my fourteenth birthday, and almost two years since I had enjoyed my eventful fortnight in Cottingham; mum and I had just returned from a shopping trip which had secured me a pair of much-needed football boots. We were in a jovial mood. A feast for two beckoned, which included a Knickerbockerglory. Alas, the telephone call quickly put paid to our good humour and all thoughts of food. I heard mum's voice falter just seconds after she lifted up the receiver. The subsequent silence, and sniffles that became heart-wrenching sobs, told me something serious had occurred.

"How did it happen?" I heard her say to the caller. "What time was it? Was she alone?"

The conversation lasted a little over ten minutes, yet it felt like a lifetime had passed by the time the receiver was replaced in its cradle on the wall. After mum had composed herself, she told me that my Auntie Kathleen had died peacefully at Castle Hill Hospital, which is located on the outskirts of Cottingham. As we were paying for my boots a couple of hours earlier, she had taken her last breath. Thankfully, she wasn't alone. Uncle Jim had held her hand throughout, and her son, John, was also present.

Mum had been aware of Auntie Kathleen's deteriorating condition for a while. But she hadn't said anything to me because she didn't want me to worry and be upset. It seems her health had been a problem for a considerable period, yet she never let it get in the way of her enjoying life. In the end, her heart simply gave up and she passed away peacefully, in the company of the two men she loved the most. For me, it was the first time I had really experienced the trauma of death. My grandma died when I was five years old. My family shielded me from the pain and grief, and I emerged relatively unscathed. Then, some sixteen months after my 1977 vacation in Cottingham, Uncle Fred suddenly died. Nobody knows precisely what happened. His body was found at the side of the road one January morning. He had been cycling to RAF Leconfield when he collapsed. A ruptured spleen, no less, was the official cause of death. His passing was a sad occasion, but it wasn't an event that devastated the family. The death of Auntie Kathleen, just six months later, was a wholly different story. Losing her had a profound effect on us all, and although we didn't know it at the time, nothing would ever be quite the same again. Uncle Jim was devastated by the loss of the woman he adored. After Auntie Kathleen's funeral, he quickly became a recluse, and mum and I rarely saw him. Number thirteen was suddenly off limits, and then one day he just upped and moved away. On the rare occasions we did spend time in his company, he was not the man I knew and loved. Grief had taken a firm hold on him and, less than four years after her death, he followed Kathleen to the grave. Officially, he died from liver failure. But the family knew a different truth: his heart had been broken.

Auntie Jessie was devastated by the loss of her sister. They had a special bond that only the closest of sisters know and treasure (my wife is blessed to enjoy such a relationship with her sister). But she soldiered on, adjusted to a new life without her younger sister, and managed to live healthily and happily well into her mid-eighties. Thankfully, Kathleen's loss was cushioned by the devotion of Auntie Maureen, my mum's youngest sister, who put a protective arm around the last surviving Foster girl. But life was never the same without Kathleen in it, and she passed away in the summer of 1992 while sitting in a rocking chair at my Auntie Maureen's home. Her death signalled the end of an era.

Such grievous losses are hard to come to terms with. But gradually you do, as time's healing powers work their wonders. And so it has been for us. The family has regrouped and, as one year merges into another, we have found peace, increasingly remembering and celebrating the contributions of these people. Like so many, my aunts and uncles didn't have much in terms of material possessions. But what they did have was much more important. They were proud, working-class souls who tried to get the best out of life every day. They were 'pint half full' types and their enthusiasm and zest for life were infectious.

Never was their kindness and selflessness more evident than when the family came together.

My holiday in East Yorkshire left an indelible imprint on my life, and even after so much time has lapsed, it is a happy period I often think about. So many years after they happened, the events of 1977 continue to make me smile and, on occasion, make me weep. But more than anything, they leave me with a lasting sense of gratitude. To have had these people in my life means everything, and even though the passing of time has dimmed their faces and hushed their voices, it is only right they continue to live on. ✳

- THE END -

AUTHOR'S NOTE

DEATH LEAVES ITS MARK ON all of us in some shape and form. For some, as part of the grieving process, lengthy 'bucket lists' are created, fundraising activities supporting the wonderful work of national and local charities are embarked upon, and far-flung places – many of them the favourite haunts of the dearly departed – are often visited. Others honour loved ones in their own unique way, as I continue to do.

My own mother passed away in June 2022. She was eighty-four-years-old, and even though she needed to manage some health-related issues daily, I thought she would live forever, after all, she was one of the strongest women I have ever known. But her health was actually far more fragile than I realised, and this was something I remained unaware of until it was far too late. To compound things, she retired and moved to France almost twenty years ago, which meant she was many hundreds of miles away and not easy to reach. When the end came, I was unable to say the goodbye I would have wished, although I am left with a lot of gratitude and love, which make up for some big regrets.

So, how does one put such experiences to constructive, effective use?

In my case, it is to pen *Sunshine on my mind*, a biographical tome that is entirely based on fact, albeit some of the details have been embellished for dramatic effect. But be assured, everything detailed in the pages of this book actually happened. I have frequently recalled the escapades to family and friends ever since they occurred, and they have proven to be a regular source of joy and chastisement in equal measure. For as my Uncle Jim would often remind me (and you have discovered), I was 'a bit of a bugger'.

Rather than just be a tribute to my mum, this book is a celebration of the lives of some of those I hold most dear – my family from East Yorkshire. Their selflessness, lust for life and forgiveness gave me security, happiness and hope throughout my childhood, and this helped play a big part in defining me. That they didn't allow my irrational and bad behaviour to get in the way of them being loving relatives tells you what kind of people they were. I know I am not alone in this regard. Many families have such wonderful people within them. They are priceless – 'big characters' as a friend of mine likes to call them – therefore we must all do whatever we can to ensure such souls are never forgotten.

In remembering my late mother and relatives, and bringing them to life through the printed word, I hope you get a small snapshot of the contributions these good, honest, working-class folk made while never complaining about the cards life had dealt them. They had many outstanding qualities, some of which I have attempted to record as accurately as I can. Despite their many differences, they possessed two particular things in abundance: the joy associated with being part of a loving, extended family unit, and great pride in being born, raised, and staying connected to Cottingham and Hull – East Yorkshire men and women to the core. As am I.

Philip Yorke
June 2023

WITH GRATITUDE

BY ANY STRETCH OF THE imagination, writing a book is a major undertaking. It doesn't matter whether it is a historical fiction novel (my usual genre) or a semi-biographical account like Sunshine on my mind, no author can do everything on their own, therefore the support I have received in recent months has been very uplifting, humbling and valuable.

Close to home, there are several people to whom I would like to extend my deepest thanks. **Keith Potter** is my long-time tennis partner who I regularly put the world to rights with, often at the expense of a set, or two, on the courts of our local tennis club. One of the reasons our game is sacrificed is because of the amount of help Keith gives, and the encouragement he offers to my writing as a sense-checker and proofreader. Throughout this project, he has been hugely supportive and has gently urged me on when I have had the occasional period of writer's bloc. Thank you for everything, Keith. Your help has meant a lot. **Catherine Pincott-Allen**, herself an accomplished historical author, is also someone I am indebted to. I have got to know Catherine (and her husband, Richard) through the stories I write about a historical figure called Francis Hacker. Francis was one of the regicides of King Charles the First. Like me, Catherine has an interest in the life of Francis, and she has recently written her own historical account of his life. As well as writing under her own name, some of Catherine's work can also be found under the pseudonym 'Emmaline Severn'. When she hasn't been undertaking research and writing, Catherine has been casting an eye over *Sunshine on my mind* – helping me keep on the main road, and not get sucked into the creative cul-de-sacs that are the curse of all writers. Thank you, Catherine. Your help and encouragement have been extremely important.

Robert Longbone-Lawrence, a relative on my late mother's side, has been another invaluable source of information when it comes to the dates of births and deaths for all of my family members mentioned in the book. Robert is a dedicated family historian and has not only pieced together an extensive history of the Longbone family, going back hundreds of years but is now also actively involved in helping other families actively connect with long-lost relatives. He is an inspiring man. My cousin, **Paul Campbell**, son of my Auntie Maureen and Uncle Archie, also cast a critical eye over the manuscript before it was published. His contributions and observations are greatly welcomed and appreciated. Thank you, Paul.

Away from friends and family, a group of people I don't know – but who have earned my unwavering gratitude – have also come to the fore. **Kazia Jewitt**, daughter of Joe and Zofia Podbiereski, willingly provided me with important background information about her late parents, which gave some depth to two of the chapters in this book. What inspiring and caring people they were. **David Elliott** has also been extremely helpful. David is the son of George and Nora, the friendly and charming owners of Elliott's newsagents on Inglemire Lane – the would-be victims of my great lemonade bottle swindle. How privileged I am to be able to include some of their story in this book.

And I would also like to thank **Joanne Brooke, Margaret Fox, Alison Goode, Nick Heaford, Louise Overfield** and **Liz Thompson,** members of a Facebook group called *Cottingham: The Good Old Days*, who have acted as 'critical friends', checking the accuracy of my geographical claims, timeline, and the general credibility of the tales I have retold. Between them, several important observations were made that have improved the overall reading experience.

I have changed the names of a handful of people who feature in this story. I have done so because mention of my name after so many years may still not conjure the most positive of thoughts – and to avoid embarrassing an individual or individuals.

Of course, errors may still remain. If this is the case, then please accept my unreserved apologies. As always, only one person is ultimately to blame for anything that is erroneous: me.

PHILIP YORKE

AS A JOURNALIST, PHILIP YORKE covered major news stories and published hard-hitting investigations. His work won awards and often set news agendas.

In recent years, he has become an author writing historical fiction novels about the brutal and bloody English Civil Wars of the seventeenth century. Both of his published books have received critical acclaim. He is currently researching and writing the third part of *The Hacker Chronicles*, the five-book series about the extraordinary life of Francis Hacker, one of the three men who signed the execution warrant of King Charles the First.

Philip has a long association with FareShare UK, a charity committed to tackling food poverty and food waste. He is a passionate supporter of the charity's values. Some of the profits from *Sunshine on my mind* will be donated to support FareShare's important work in Hull and the surrounding East Yorkshire area.

Married to Julie, with whom he has five children, Philip remains a devoted and optimistic Hull City fan.

Remembering...

Fred Burgess
18 July 1918 - 3 January 1979

Kathleen Burgess (nee Foster)
22 October 1922 - 30 July 1979

Jim Burgess
12 March 1920 - 13 November 1983

Jessie Ellis (nee Foster)
12 June 1906 - 14 August 1992

Archie Campbell
11 February 1935 - 16 August 1994

Brenda Hauerslev (nee Longbone)
16 October 1941 - 23 March 1998

Ian Longbone
16 October 1941 - 16 December 2009

Maureen Campbell (nee Longbone)
20 August 1948 - 25 December 2015

Ann Measures (nee Longbone)
19 December 1938 - 28 June 2022

Printed in Great Britain
by Amazon

38008829R00111